Prehistoric
ATLAS

Photographs by Giovanni Pinna, Luciano Spezia and from Vallardi Archive (12 top, 17 left, 22 top, 23, 65 centre left, 77 centre); Arduini-Teruzzi (13 centre, 16 left, 30, 31, 59 bottom left, 64 centre, 69 bottom left); Coleman (65 top); Austrian State Tourist office (80 top right); Erwin Christian (62–63); Enrico Giovenzana (16a); Intitute of Geological Sciences London (12 bottom, 13 left); Marka (8, 9, 17 right, 21 right, 22, 41 right, 46–47, 51 top, 57, 61 bottom, 68 top, 70–71, 72 bottom, 75 bottom left, right); Mazza (79 centre, bottom); Musée de l'Homme, Paris (76 top, 77 bottom left, right); Museo di Geologia e Paleontologia, University of Florence (73 right, top/bottom); Museo di Paleontologia, Rome (72–73 top, 75 top — photo Schiavinotto); National Museums of Kenya (76–77 top, 77 centre); Publiaerfoto (74 top); The Royal Scottish Museum, Edinburgh (53 top).

This edition published in 1994 by Blitz Editions
an imprint of Bookmart Limited, Registered Number 2372865.
Trading as Bookmart Limited, Desford Road, Enderby,
Leicester LE9 5AD

ISBN 1 85605 220 6

Printed in Italy by Vallardi Industrie Grafiche S.p.A.
Lainate (MI) - June 1994

Prehistoric
ATLAS

P. Arduini and G. Teruzzi

Contents

The Story of Life

The story of life on Earth resembles a spiral: follow it and we can trace the main stages of evolution through which the animal and vegetable worlds passed on the way to their present state.

The Earth was formed about four and a half thousand million years ago. However, only after the Earth's crust had hardened and the atmosphere and hydrosphere were formed (though not with the same properties they have now) were the conditions created for life to appear about three thousand million years ago. The first living forms evolved in the oceans; they were very simple organisms and for a long time remained microscopic in size. This was the period of colonies of unicellular blue-green algae, the stromatolites. Only just before the start of the Palaeozoic Era did more complex organisms appear that were visible to the naked eye: jellyfish (Medusae), worms and molluscs. The Palaeozoic Era, which began about 570 million years ago, saw marine life thriving; invertebrates were especially widespread, such as trilobites, graptolites and brachiopods, and very soon the first vertebrates, the Agnatha, emerged. An event of great importance took place about 400 million years ago, when the land above sea-level was colonised by the first vascular plants and the first invertebrates. A little later, in the Devonian Period, the vertebrates also left their water environment and together with the amphibians took their first steps on dry land. From the amphibians evolved the reptiles, who were the dominant creatures of the era that followed, the Mesozoic. They developed not only terrestrial forms, like the dinosaurs, but also flying forms, with the pterosaurs, and marine forms, with the ichthyosaurs and plesiosaurs. The most widespread of marine invertebrates in the Mesozoic Era were ammonites, cephalopod molluscs. The Mesozoic also saw the appearance of mammals and birds. They became fully developed only after the biological crisis at the end of the Era which resulted in the disappearance of the big reptiles. During the Cenozoic Era which followed, both vegetable and animal organisms took on an appearance increasingly like that of the present day. The first Hominids were comparative latecomers — they did not appear until the Quaternary Period, about 2 million years ago.

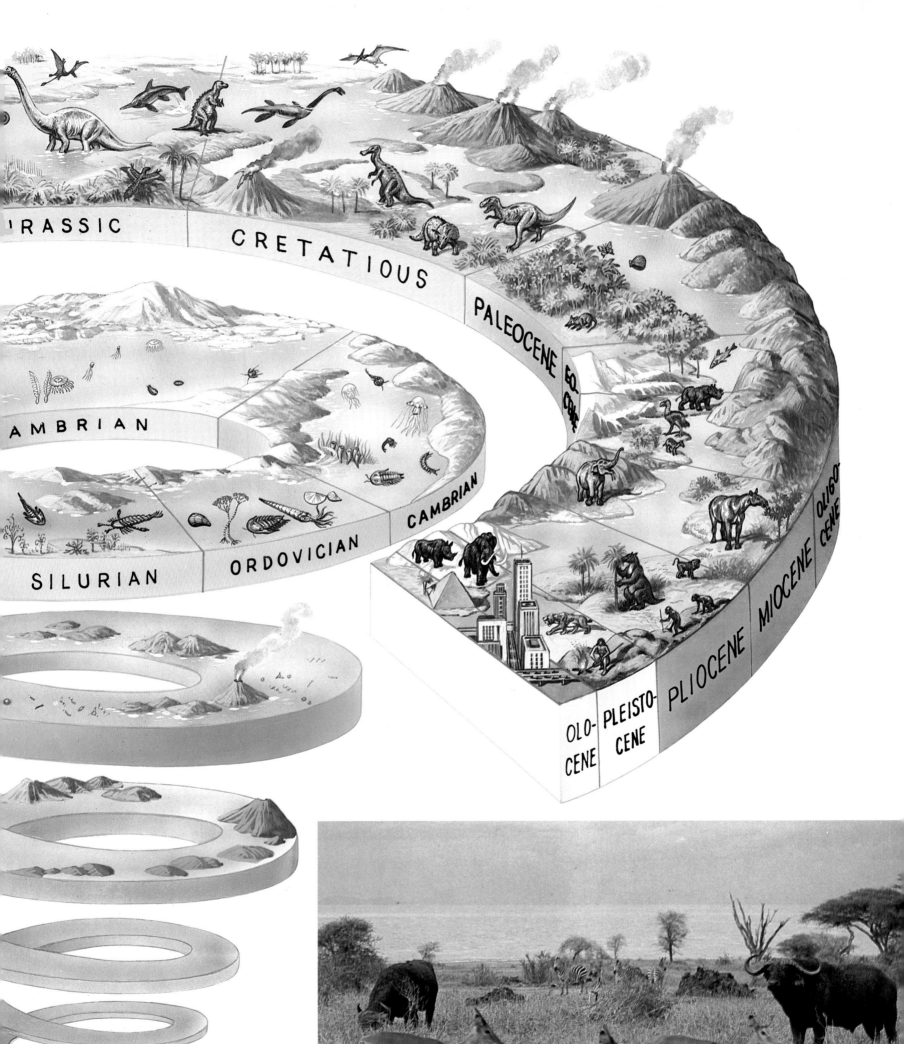

JRASSIC

CRETATIOUS

PALEOCENE

EO-CENE

CAMBRIAN

AMBRIAN

SILURIAN

ORDOVICIAN

CAMBRIAN

OLI-GO-CENE

MIOCENE

PLIOCENE

PLEISTO-CENE

OLO-CENE

The Geological Eras

Plant columns (left to right): CONIFERS · GINGKOS · ANGIOSPERMAE · CYCADALES · PTERIDOSPERMS · EARLY FERNS · FILICALES · LYCOPODIALES · HORSETAILS · ALGAE/MUSHROOMS/MOSSES · BACTERIA

ERA	MILLIONS OF YEARS AGO	PERIOD
QUATERNARY Appearance of Homo Sapiens. Great glaciations of the Ice Ages.	2	HOLOCENE PLEISTOCENE
CENOZOIC Appearance of Australopithecus. First apes.	22	PLIOCENE MIOCENE OLIGOCENE
Spread of macroscopic foraminifera in the seas. Appearance of the first horses and elephants. Spread of birds and mammals.	65	EOCENE PALAEOCENE
MESOZOIC Start of mountain orogenesis. Disappearance of the dinosaurs, the ammonites, flying reptiles and giant marine reptiles. First marsupial and placental mammals.	140	CRETACEOUS
Widespread nature of dinosaurs. First flowering plants. First birds. First teleost fish. Spread of ammonites.	195	JURASSIC
First mammals. First tortoises and turtles. Appearance of first dinosaurs, flying reptiles and marine reptiles.	230	TRIASSIC
PALAEOZOIC Formation of a single great continent on Earth. Extinction of trilobites and other invertebrates. First reptile-mammals.	280	PERMIAN
First reptiles. Extinction of graptolites. Great expansion of forests. Appearance of the first gymnosperms. Start of Caledonian orogenesis.	345	CARBONIFEROUS
First terrestrial vertebrates: the amphibians. Appearance of the ammonites. Development of forests: first plants with seeds. First sharks. Armoured fish.	395	DEVONIAN
End of Hercynian orogenesis. Life on land above sea-level: first plants and first terrestrial invertebrates.	435	SILURIAN
Appearance of the vertebrates. First corals. Start of Hercynian (or Variscan) orogenesis. First cephalopods. First graptolites.	500	ORDOVICIAN
Appearance of invertebrates: arthropods, mollusca, sponges, echinoderms.	570	CAMBRIAN
ARCHAEOZOIC First organisms visible to the naked eye.		ALGONKIAN
First signs of life.	4500	ARCHAEAN

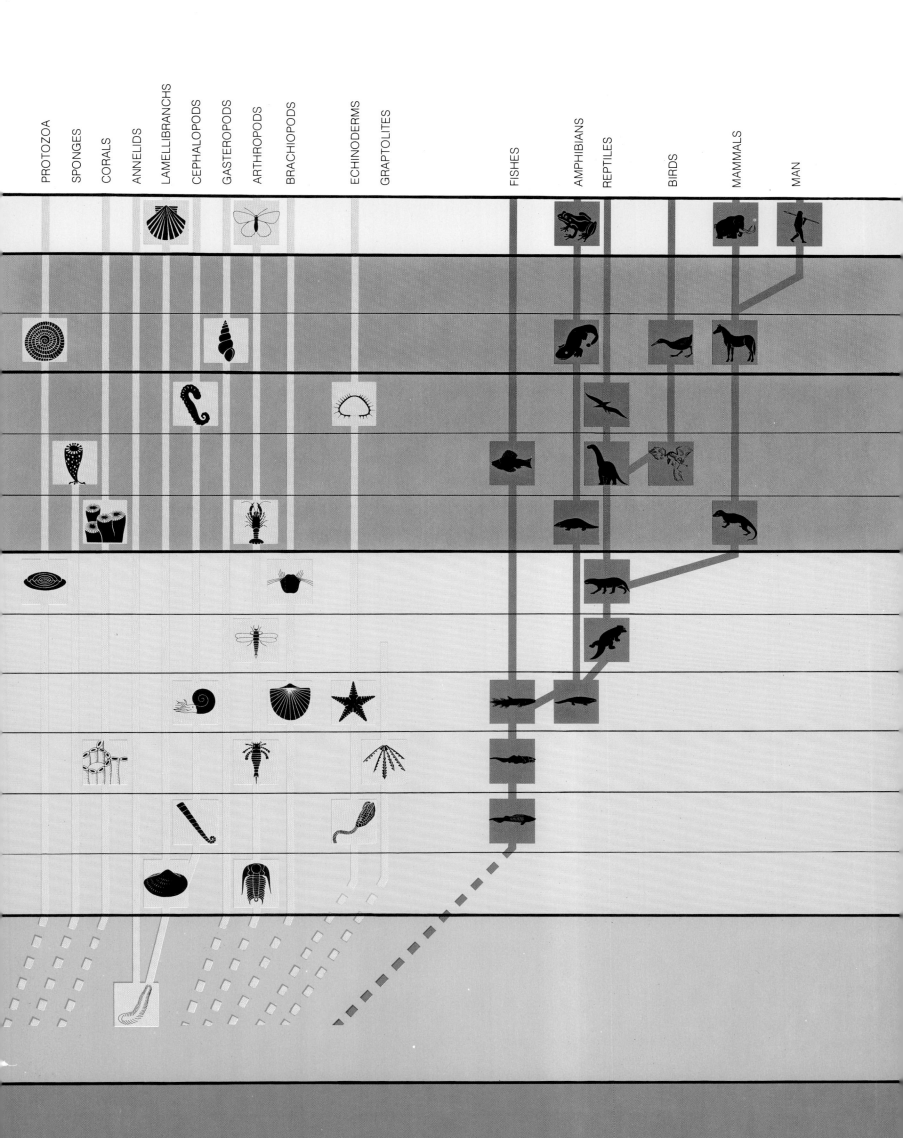

PROTOZOA

SPONGES

CORALS

ANNELIDS

LAMELLIBRANCHS

CEPHALOPODS

GASTEROPODS

ARTHROPODS

BRACHIOPODS

ECHINODERMS

GRAPTOLITES

FISHES

AMPHIBIANS

REPTILES

BIRDS

MAMMALS

MAN

The Age of the Earth

Imagine the inside of our planet as a series of concentric casings whose thickness increases the closer you get to the centre of the Earth. Moving outwards from the Earth's core, there are three main sectors: the core, the mantle and the crust. The core and the mantle make up most of the Earth's mass, while the crust forms a skin varying in thickness from 5 to 50 kilometres: this is very thin compared to the Earth's radius of about 6378 kilometres at the Equator. The outcrops of rock on the Earth's surface can be divided up, according to their formation; they are:

a) *magmatic rocks*, deriving from magmas cooling beneath the crust, and being forced up through the crust;

b) *sedimentary rocks*, from the depositing of products left after the disintegration of previous rocks, or formed by chemical deposits, or by living organisms, as in coral reefs;

c) *metamorphic rocks*, deriving from the transformation of rocks buried beneath the Earth's crust which undergo mineralogical changes because of the high temperatures and pressures to which they are subjected. Other metamorphic rocks are formed by contact between the magmas and the crust rocks.

The Earth's crust is not stable: it is fragmented into rigid lumps which are continually moving on top of each other. At some points, one lump may slip underneath another and disappear into the mantle. Elsewhere, new crust is formed by magmas rising up from the mantle. In this way, the rocks of the Earth's crust never stop forming, disintegrating, and changing their properties.

▦	KAIBAB LIMESTONE
▦	TOROWEAP FORMATION
▦	COCONINO SANDSTONE
▦	HERMIT CLAY-SCHISTS
▦	SUPAI GROUP
▦	REDWALL LIMESTONE
▦	TEMPLE BUTTE LIMESTONE
▦	MUAV LIMESTONE
▦	BRIGHT ANGEL CLAY-SCHISTS
▦	TAPEATS SANDSTONE

PERMIAN

CARBONIFEROUS

DEVONIAN

CAMBRIAN

PRECAMBRIAN

GNEISS AND VISHNU SCHIST

COLORADO RIVER

A fracture of the crust

By analysing the layers of the Earth's crust, geologists can reconstruct the different phases in the history of the crust and of living organisms of the past. One of the best known outcrops of rocks is the spectacular Grand Canyon in Colorado. Here, as you can see in the drawing on the left, it is possible to identify a succession of horizontal layers of rock deposited during the Palaeozoic Era: these rest on a base of older rocks that were subject to secondary folding and erosion during the Archaeozoic Era. The strata of rocks are grouped according to their characteristics and labelled with the names given to them by geologists.

Geological maps

The drawing on the left is a schematic geological map of the region round Lake Lugano in Switzerland and Italy. Here, there is a famous fossil-bearing layer dating back to the Triassic Period (broken red line). The different colours on the map illustrate the various rocks which outcrop or exist beneath the vegetation cover. By examining the geological map, we can reconstruct the periods of this area's geological history, shown schematically in the drawing on the right. Over a base layer of pre-Palaeozoic rock (1) are deposits of lava left there during the Permian. At the start of the Triassic, the sea flooded the region and began depositing sedimentary rocks (2), among them are fossil-bearing rocks in a reef (3). Rocks continued to be deposited in the sea throughout the Mesozoic Era (4) before being raised, folded and eroded during the formation of the Alps. At this time, the Alps took on their present form and position (5). The photo beneath shows a fish from the Besano–Monte San Giorgio deposit.

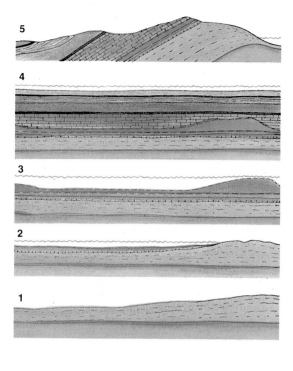

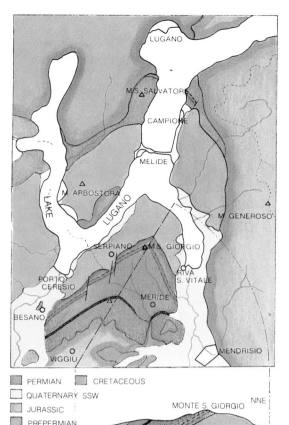

Legend:
- PERMIAN
- QUATERNARY
- JURASSIC
- PREPERMIAN
- TRIASSIC
- CRETACEOUS

SSW — MONTE S. GIORGIO — NNE

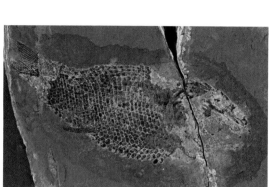

Legend:
- JURASSIC
- TRIASSIC
- ICHTHYOLITHIC SCHISTS AND REEF FROM MONTE S. SALVATORE
- CRETACEOUS
- PERMIAN

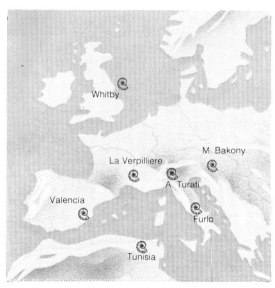

The dating of rocks

The dating of rocks uses techniques which differ with the age, chemical composition and origin of the rocks themselves. In geology, there is widespread use of the so-called 'absolute' dating methods which rely on the radioactive isotopes contained in the rocks. Using these methods, magmatic rocks can be dated, whereas sedimentary rocks are not usually datable. To get datings for very recent rocks, other methods are also used, among them the varve method: varves are thin layers of lake deposits with alternating light and dark seams, each pair of which represents a time-interval equalling one year.

The photo above shows some of the oldest rocks yet found, dating back over 3,500 million years.

Dating by fossils

A fair proportion of the rocks which outcrop on the Earth's surface are sedimentary rocks. Since their age cannot be measured by direct dating, the method used is indirect; one way concentrates on the succession of fossils they contain. An organism is actually a distinguishing feature of a given period in the Earth's history, and if it is found in a rock, that tells us in which period the rock itself was formed. Particularly useful in this context are the so-called index or guide fossils, which invariably had a short life-span and a wide geographical spread: thus it is possible to date and link together even those rocks which are very far apart. Take for instance the case of the *Hildoceras* genus of ammonite (above), which lived during the Lower Jurassic. As the map on the right shows, this fossil has been discovered in various parts of Europe and North Africa, in rocks which must therefore be of the same age.

The erosion cycle

The morphology of the Earth is continually changing, owing to the action of erosive agents. In fact, from the moment they were formed, the mountains began to break up from the effects of freezing and thawing, chemical erosion, and the action of water. The products of this breaking-up are then carried by rivers and the wind and deposited in lakes and lowlands, reaching as far as the sea. There they form accumulations of sediment which then give rise to new rocks.

The spectrometer

In the photo on the left is a special apparatus called a 'mass spectrometer'. This can date rock samples by analysing the radioactive isotopes they contain. By this means, the ages of even the oldest rocks can be calculated accurately in millions of years.

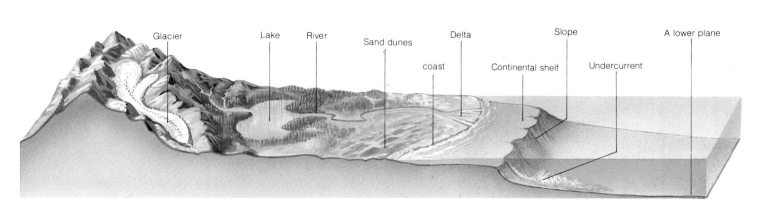

Labels: Glacier, Lake, River, Sand dunes, Delta, Slope, A lower plane, coast, Continental shelf, Undercurrent

CAMBRIAN
570 million years ago

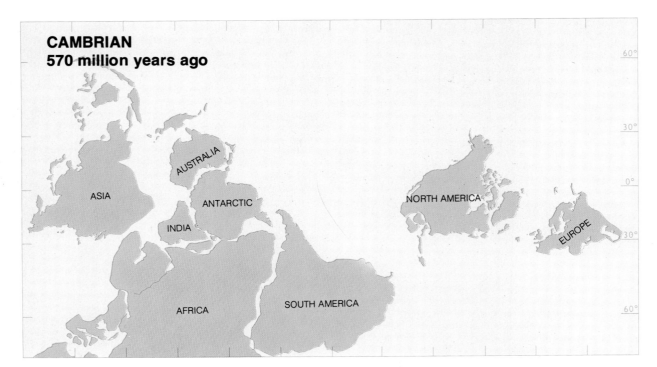

During past geological eras, the position of the continents and oceans has undergone continual change. The map (left) shows how the continents looked during the Cambrian Period about 570 million years ago. The continents we know today did not then exist. Instead, there were four separate continental land masses, with deep seas in between. These four corresponded to Europe, North America, Asia and a fourth continent uniting present day South America, Africa, Australia, the Antarctic, India and Madagascar.

CARBONIFEROUS
340 million years ago

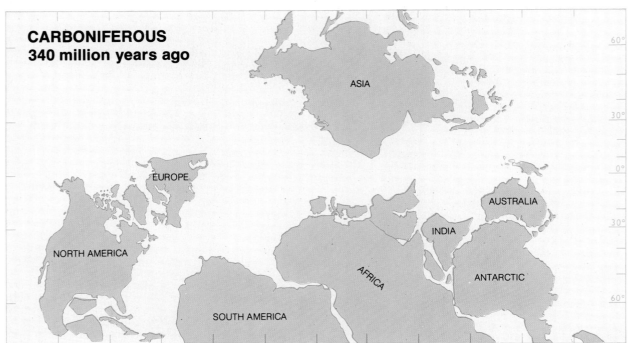

During the Carboniferous Period, about 340 million years ago, Europe was joined to North America, and the continents of the Southern Hemisphere formed a single continental land mass separate from the other continents. Asia was on its own. When Asia and Europe combined this led later to the formation of the Urals range of mountains.

PERMIAN
280 million years ago

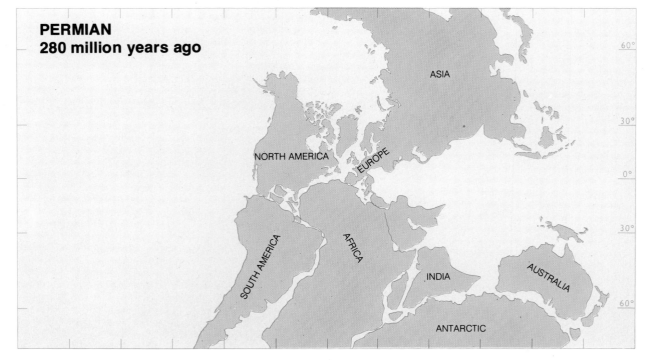

During the Permian Period, about 280 million years ago, and until the start of the Mesozoic Era, the continents came together in a single mass, thus forming a sort of 'supercontinent' called Pangaea. This great continent was breached on its Eastern side by an oceanic gulf called Tethys.

f the Past

The present lay-out of the continents came about largely as a result of events during the Tertiary Period. The movement of the African land mass northwards and of India north-eastwards resulted in their union with the Euroasian continent: this gave rise to the spectacular foldings of the Earth's crust that led to the formation of the Alps and the Himalayas. In the meantime, Australia also shifted northwards, pivoting round its own axis until it reached its present position. The Atlantic Ocean was still in the process of widening, whereas the Pacific was being reduced by the forward movement of the two Americas and the Asian archipelagos.

The Present Layout of the Continents

During the Eocene, about 50 million years ago, and following the break-up of the single continent, which occurred in the Mesozoic and led to the opening up of the Atlantic Ocean, in the Jurassic, the lay-out of the continents was almost the same as it is today: the Antarctic, however, was still joined to Australia, while India had not yet come into contact with the continent of Asia.

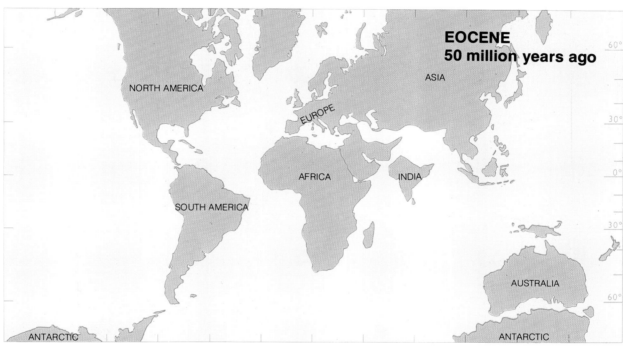

**EOCENE
50 million years ago**

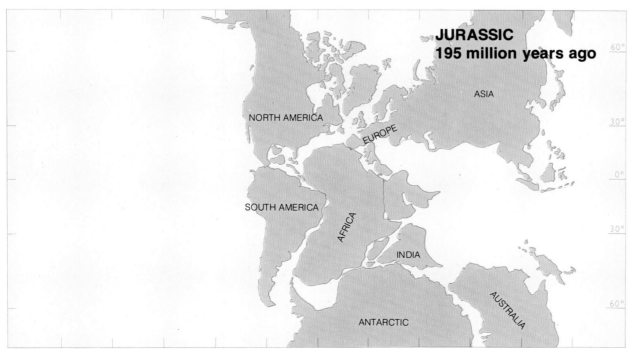

**JURASSIC
195 million years ago**

The single continent of Pangaea had already began to break up by the beginning of the Mesozoic Era, about 220 million years ago. As a result, two main continental land masses took shape; a Northern one, known as Laurasia, made up of North America, Europe and Asia, and a Southern one, Gondwanaland, consisting of South America, Africa, India, the Antarctic and Australia. Africa and South America had already begun to separate off from the other continental land masses of Gondwanaland during the Triassic.

15

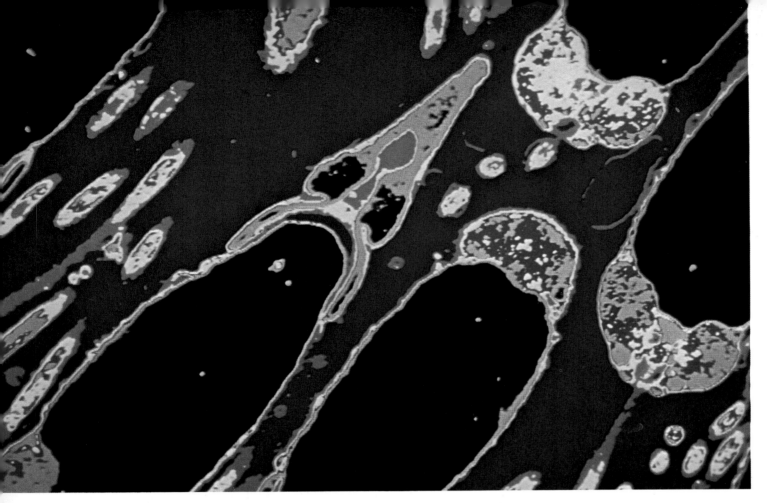

Evolution

The celebrated and still controversial theory of evolution by natural selection resulted from the work of Charles Darwin. By studying the different forms of life that populate our world, and by observing fossil faunas, Darwin deduced that animal species are not fixed and immutable entities as had previously been thought. On the contrary, a species can change with time, giving rise to variations in form. Darwin also saw that habitat, in the physical and organic sense, exercises a kind of selection that favours the survival of those forms which can best adapt themselves to it. Before Darwin, others, such as Frenchman Jean-Baptiste Lamarck, had observed that different forms of life had undergone evolution through time. However, none of these observers had managed with the same precision as Darwin to develop a theory explaining these transformations in the living world. The Darwinian theory of evolution marked a new frontier in the biological sciences. It paved the way for a long series of studies aimed at uncovering the links between present and past forms of life, and the processes which make variation possible within species, as well as the patterns through which natural selection operates. A substantial boost to the evolutionist theory came with the discovery of the laws of Mendel on the inheriting of characteristics which enabled the subsequent developments in genetics.

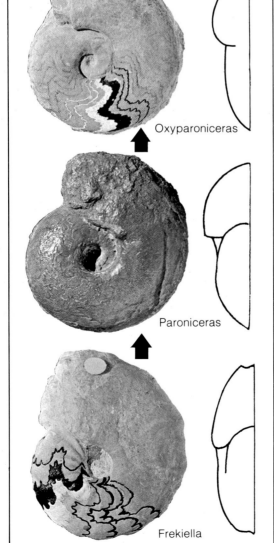

Oxyparoniceras

Paroniceras

Frekiella

Fossils and evolution
Fossils give us the best evidence about evolution: in the illustration (left), we can see the successive forms brought about by evolution in a group of ammonites from the Lower Jurassic. The genus *Frekiella* gave rise to the genus *Paroniceras*, from which the genus *Oxyparoniceras* evolved.

The picture on the right reconstructs the evolution of the skull in the Titanotheres — mammals who lived in the Cenozoic.

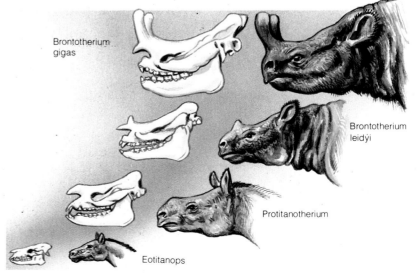

Brontotherium gigas

Brontotherium leidyi

Protitanotherium

Eotitanops

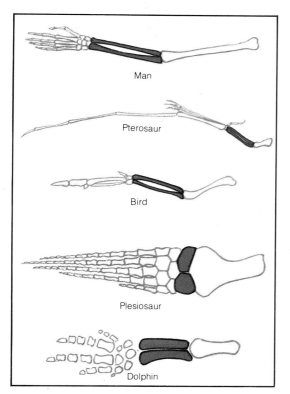

Modifications to limbs and evolutionary convergence

The drawing on the left represents the modifications to the bones of the upper limbs which took place in different groups of animals as they adapted to their environment. Working upwards from the bottom, we can see how the bones in the dolphin's forearm, the radius and the ulna, are robust and very similar, whereas the 'hand' has only slightly developed phalanxes. In the plesiosaur, however, there was a drastic reduction of the radius and the ulna, and the development of the hyperphalanxy which enables this marine reptile to use its 'hand' like a paddle. The difference between these two limbs is due to the fact that, unlike plesiosaurs, dolphins use their fore-limbs only as a rudder because the force that propels them is provided by their tail. The different arrangement of the same bones in the limb of a bird and a pterosaur is also self-evident if one considers that birds need a strong limb to be able to soar in the air, whereas pterosaurs were restricted to gliding, letting themselves drop from a height off rocks or branches. The man's arm seems the least specialised, but it is this which gives it maximum versatility. On the right, there are illustrations of three groups of animals phylogenetically far removed from each other. Nevertheless, by occupying the same ecological niche they have achieved the same form through evolutionary convergence: the dolphin, a marine mammal; the ichthyosaur, a marine reptile; the tuna or tunny, a teleost fish.

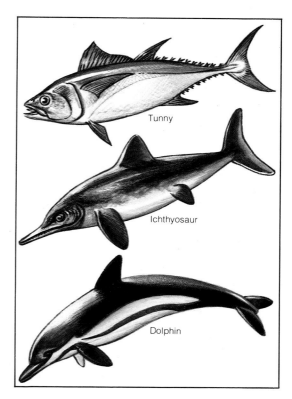

Darwin

Charles Darwin was born in England in 1809 and died in 1882. He was educated first in Edinburgh and then at Cambridge, where he met some of the leading naturalists of the day, among them the distinguished Scots geologist Sir Charles Lyell who had a great influence on him.

The voyage of the *Beagle*

In 1831, after finishing his studies, Darwin embarked on the brig *Beagle*, a ship equipped for scientific research, which took him on a round-the-world journey lasting five years. By the end of it, he had collected a huge amount of materials and notes. These later enabled him to develop his theory of evolution by natural selection. Among the many places Darwin visited, one in particular provided him with an opportunity to make some remarkable observations — the Galapagos archipelago. These islands are actually populated by animal species which incorporate a number of varieties, each characteristic of an individual island, as in the case of the iguanas (see photo, right). This fact contributed to the theory that these varieties were due to a separate evolution of different animal populations deriving from the same stock, following their isolation from each other.

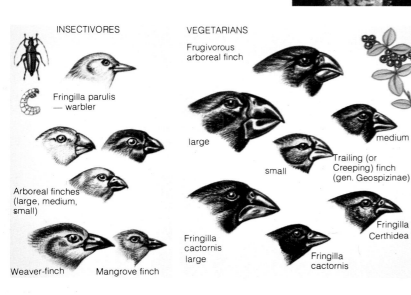

Darwin's chaffinches

Another group of creatures Darwin observed on the Galapagos were the chaffinches (see drawings, left). He noticed that each of the islands was inhabited by a species of chaffinch, all deriving from the same stock, but which in the habitat of any one island had developed varieties which differed according to the ecological niches they had occupied. Some of them were insectivores, in fact, while others had developed a strong beak adapted to a diet based on seeds.

The Galapagos

Darwin's route to the Galapagos islands (below) situated off the coast of Ecuador.

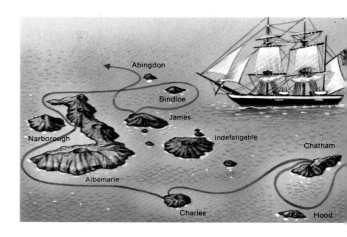

17

How Fossils were formed

A fossilisation process is the chemical-physical process whose effect on animal or plant remains has preserved them up until the present. Take, for example, a mollusc which has an outer shell, like the gasteropods. When a mollusc died, the tender parts which made up the body would be attacked by necrophagous organisms. Only the shell would be left. On the sea bed, this shell would be covered by sediment and then subjected to the action of the water content of the sediment: it might be dissolved, or undergo fossilisation. Fossilisation, however, is a wholly exceptional occurrence and happens only in particular conditions.

The most important fossilisation processes are:
—impregnation
—integral conservation
—substitution or mineralisation

FOSSILISATION BY IMPREGNATION

Evidence of this process can be found in vertebrates whose bones are reticulated structures composed of calcium phosphate and where tissue is inside the vacuoles. Take the case of a mammal which died near a lake or on a seashore. Its body, once carried into the water, would have been dragged by currents out to sea where it would settle on a shoal. Here, the porous bones were open to impregnation: salts dissolved in the sediment water could find their way into the pores, saturating them and fossilising the skeleton. The process usually occurs in the sea, but not infrequently in riverbeds and lakes as well.

INTEGRAL FOSSILISATION

Fossilisation by integral preservation is much rarer; it happens, for instance, in caves which have been completely blocked by a landslide. The animals trapped inside could not have fallen victim to predators nor, through the lack of oxygen, to organisms which quickly cause them to decompose, so, they would have undergone a process known as mummification.

Amber provides another method of integral fossilisation. Amber is resin, produced naturally from trees, which, as it runs down the trunks, gathers up any insects in its path. Preservation in amber is especially interesting because even the most minute structures of the insects are included. Another very rare kind of integral fossilisation occurs where the preservative is a glacier: freezing in a glacier led, for example, to the discovery of a mammoth in

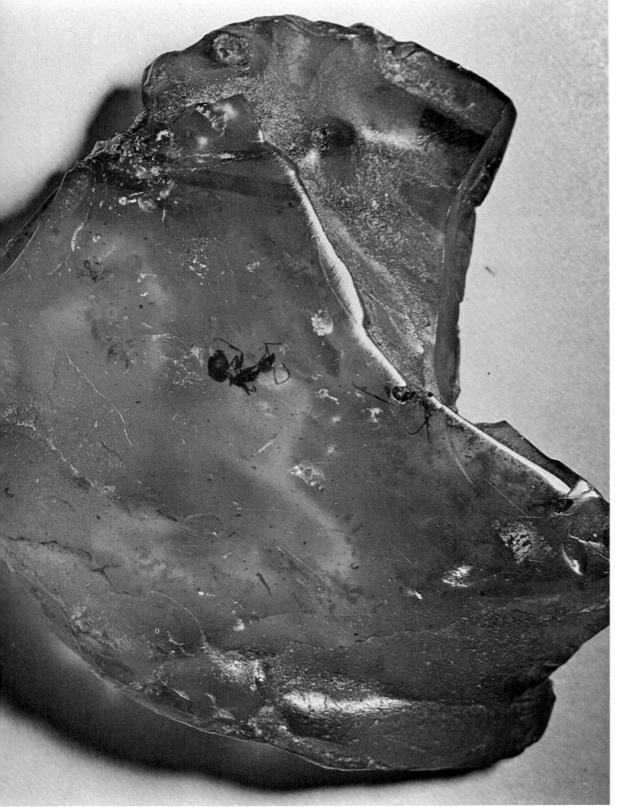

Two typical aspects of fossilisation; left: an insect preserved in amber from the Baltic, from the Oligocene Epoch; below: the skull of an *Ursus spelaeus* from the Quaternary Period, found in the Po valley in Italy.

18

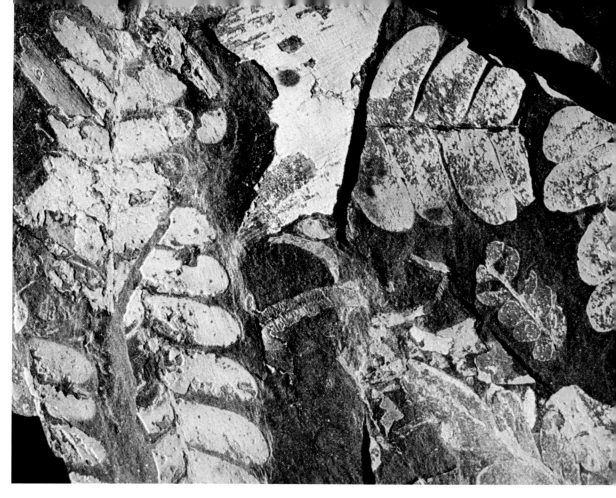

the glaciers of Siberia. This has afforded evidence that these European creatures sported a thick coat of fur during the cold phases of the Quaternary. This fact came to light only through the process of integral preservation.

FOSSILISATION BY SUBSTITUTION
The substitution process occurs chiefly in the skeletons of animals. These most often consist of calcite or aragonite, or more rarely, of silica.

A calcite shell is found fossilised much less often than an aragonite one, since calcite is much more stable than aragonite as regards sediment. It is therefore possible to observe calcitised fossils which originally had an aragonite shell: the calcite crystals substituted for the aragonite crystals can be seen in close-up under the microscope, arranged in a different pattern from those which made up the original shell.

The abundance of magnesium in marine waters gives rise to the formation of dolomitised fossils, and in the same way the presence of sulphides on the sea bottom produces pyritised fossils. The fossilisation method therefore depends on the 'salt' present in the sediment, salt which will then go to substitute or increase the minute crystals which make up the skeletal structures of invertebrates, vertebrates and plants.

Above left: one of the now extinct cephalopod mulluscs, *Belemnoidea*, fossilised in vivianite. Above: a group of leaves fossilised in talcum. Fossilisation in vivianite, and in talcum, are both quite rare.

Below: this sun-coloured disc is a calyx of coral fossilised in silica. The original structures can still be seen.

Above: an example of limonitised ammonite, fossils which are quite rare if authentic. Below: a marvellous sectioned ammonite showing how waters percolating through the sediment have deposited magnificent calcite crystals inside it.

Below: an echinoderm, a fossil from Australia, commonly called a sea-urchin, fossilised in azurite.

Above: two ammonites with their original shells. Below: a gasteropod showing chalcedony crystals formed inside.

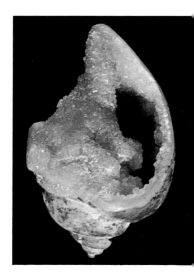

19

The Past in the Earth

ARCHAEOZOIC ERA

Swaziland (*south Africa*) Microfossils dating back to about 3,000 million years ago.
Ediacara (*south Australia*) Earliest remains of living organisms visible to the naked eye: jellyfish, worms and as yet unidentified animals.

PALAEOZOIC ERA

Burgess (*Canada*) Clayey schists with trilobites and other arthropods, as well as soft-bodied organisms: annelids, onychophores, priapulids and other organisms as yet unknown (Cambrian).
Bohemia (*Czechoslovakia*) Deposits with numerous trilobites (Cambrian).
Bundenbach (*Silesia*) Black schists with echinoderms, trilobites, graptolites, sponges and jellyfish (Ordovician).
Dudley (*England*) Limestones with several remains of invertebrates (Silurian).
Scotland (*Great Britain*) Deposits with armoured and crossopterygian fish (Devonian).
Scaumenac Bay (*Greenland*) Deposits with shellfish and the first amphibians, among them Ichthyostega (Devonian).
Mazon Creek (*USA*) Found in nodules of siderite, plants, fish, crustaceans and invertebrates minus their hard parts: annelids, priapulids, jellyfish etc. (Carboniferous).
Kilkenny (*Ireland*) Continental type of deposits, with abundant remains of plants and animals living in the great forests (Carboniferous).
Autun (*France*) Deposit of amphibians, including branchiosauri (Permian).
Itarare (*Brazil*) Deposits containing numerous reptile mesosaurs (Permian).
Sosio (*Sicily*) Marine deposit with cephalopods and other invertebrates (Permian).
Karroo (*south Africa*) Deposits in the Karroo Desert with a rich fauna of tetrapods, in particular reptile-mammals (Permian).

MESOZOIC ERA

Besano — M. San Giorgio (*Italy*–*Switzerland*) Bituminous schists with the remains of numerous terrestrial and marine reptiles, invertebrates — cephalopods and lamellibranchs — and plants (Triassic).
Elgin (*Scotland*) Rich deposit of aquatic vertebrates. Mid-Triassic reptile fauna.
Ischigualasto (*Argentina*) Deposit with a rich fauna of reptiles (Triassic).
Holzmaden (*Germany*) Marls very rich in marine reptiles, among them big ichthyosaurs, crocodiles, and plesiosaurs. Among the invertebrates, ammonites and enormous sea lilies (Jurassic).
Lyme Regis (*Great Britain*) Numerous reptiles, among them plesiosaurs and ichthyosaurs, fish and invertebrates (Jurassic).
Osteno (*Italy*) Limestones with plants, fish and numerous invertebrates including those with soft bodies; crustaceans, cephalopods, and annelids (Jurassic).
Yorkshire (*Great Britain*) The cliffs along the North Sea coast are famous for the abundant faunas of ammonites and other invertebrates (Jurassic).
La Verpilliere (*France*) Classic site with pyritised and limonitised ammonites (Jurassic).
Solnhofen (*Germany*) Found in lithographic limestone, the earliest bird, flying reptiles and land reptiles; fish, invertebrates and plants in large numbers (Jurassic).

Wyoming (*USA*) Deposit of dinosaurs with allosaurus and camptosaurus (Jurassic).
Tendaguru (*Tanzania*) Deposit with rich dinosaur fauna, among them the armoured dinosaurs (Jurassic).
Bernissart (*Belgium*) Discovery of remains of iguanodons which had mysteriously fallen into a ravine (Cretaceous).
Gadoufaua (*Niger*) Fossil-bearing strata which outcrop for 150 kilometres and contain the remains of numerous dinosaurs (Cretaceous).
Gobi Desert (*Mongolia*) Rich deposit of dinosaurs (Cretaceous).
Utah and Ontario (*USA-Canada*) Deposits with the remains of hundreds of dinosaurs, among them tyrannosaurus, brontosaurus, triceratops and duck-billed dinosaur (Cretaceous).
Bahia Blanca (*Argentina*) Numerous fish, including the last fossil coelacanths, and insects (Cretaceous).
Hakel and Sahel Alma (*Lebanon*) Limestone with an abundance of fish, crustaceans, annelids and cephalopods (Cretaceous).
Aix en Provence (*France*) Deposit noted for its many dinosaur eggs (Cretaceous).
Barreme (*France*) Limestone with abundant remains of cephalopods, including developed ammonites (Cretaceous).

CENOZOIC ERA

Fayum (*Egypt*) Remains of numerous mammals, among them the first sirenids, the first cetaceans and the oldest proboscideans (Eocene–Oligocene).
Monte Bolca (*Italy*) Deposit noted for the quantity and magnificence of its fish. Crustaceans and plants also discovered there (Eocene).
Messel (*Germany*) Rich continental fauna of mammals, birds, crocodiles and fish (Eocene).
Paris (*France*) In the gypsa of Montmartre, numerous remains of mammals, among them Palaeotherium, and birds (Eocene).
S. Dakota (*USA*) In the Bad Lands formation, outcrops of abundant remains of mammals, such as oreodon and rhinoceros, tortoises and turtles (Oligocene).
Baltic Sea (*Denmark*) The shores and shoals of the Baltic have yielded up fossil resins containing insects (Oligocene).
Mainz (*Germany*) In the Mainz Basin, deposits noted for mammal faunas, including rhinoceros, dinotherium and Hipparion (Oligocene-Miocene).
Virginia (*USA*) Marine faunas with the remains of the teeth of fish and marine invertebrates, especially mollusca (Pliocene).
Castell 'Arquato (*Italy*) Clays with marine invertebrates and skeletons of cetaceans (Pliocene).

QUATERNARY ERA

Rancho La Brea (*USA*) Asphalt lakes with birds deposited in the bitumen, including vultures, and also mammals, among them the sabre-toothed tiger (Pleistocene).
Valdarno (*Italy*) Abundant remains of continental vertebrates, such as elephants, rhinoceros, hippopotami and suidians (Pleistocene).
Pampas (*Argentina*) The fossil remains of the Pampas comprise skeletons of the giant megatherium and the carapaces of the great xenarthrans (Pleistocene).
Madagascar The famous eggs of Aepyornis, the great bird which could not fly (Pleistocene–Holocene).
Siberia The mammoths of Siberia constitute a rare instance of fossilisation in ice (Pleistocene).

● ARCHAEOZOIC

● PALAEOZOIC

● MESOZOIC

● CENOZOIC

● QUATERNARY

The deposit of Mazon Creek

In the deposit at Mazon Creek, in the state of Illinois (USA), the remains were discovered of a number of organisms which lived in the Upper Carboniferous in a brackish water habitat. The fossils were found in coal mines, inside the characteristic nodules of siderite (an oxide of iron) and comprise a large variety of animals including soft-bodied animals. In addition to fish and crustaceans, there were worms, jellyfish, spiders and insects. There was no lack of plants. Typical of the deposit is Tullymonstrum, a bizarre-shaped animal that does not fit into any known present-day group.

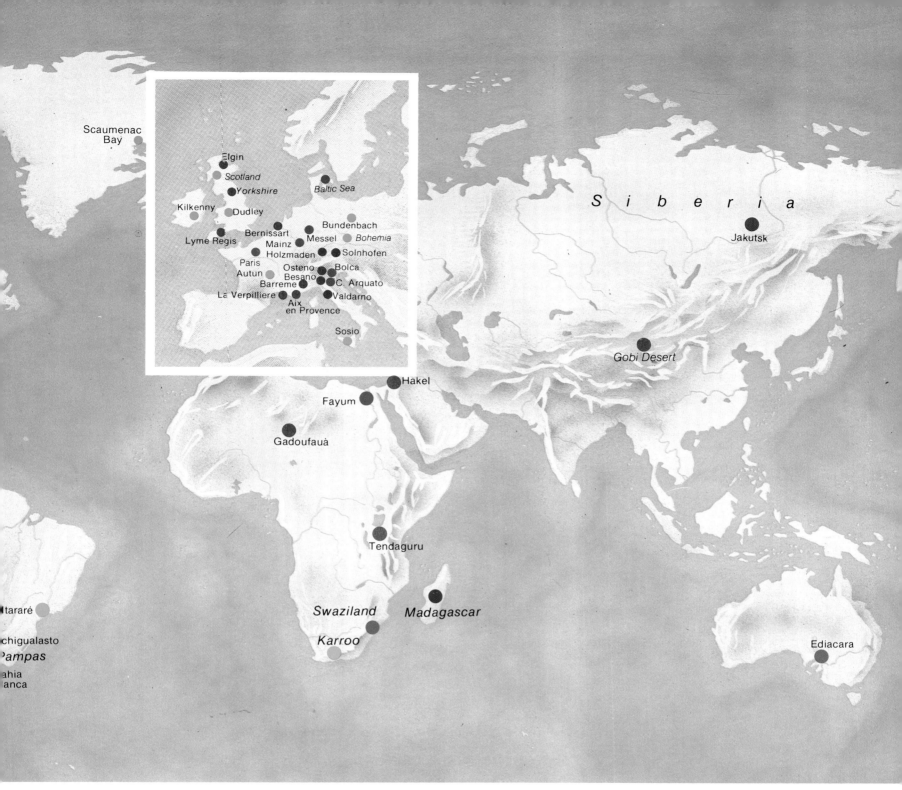

Scaumenac Bay

Elgin
Scotland
Yorkshire
Baltic Sea
Kilkenny
Dudley
Bundenbach
Bernissart
Mainz
Messel
Bohemia
Lyme Regis
Holzmaden
Solnhofen
Paris
Osteno
Bolca
Autun
Besano
Barreme
C. Arquato
La Verpilliere
Valdarno
Aix en Provence
Sosio

Siberia

Jakutsk

Gobi Desert

Hakel
Fayum

Gadoufauà

Tendaguru

Swaziland
Madagascar
Karroo

tararé
chigualasto
Pampas
ahia
anca

Ediacara

The Solnhofen deposit
Solnhofen and other sites in a Bavarian valley (Germany) have become famous through fossil discoveries in 'lithographic limestone'. This name derived from the use of limestone in printing. The fossils settled here during the Upper Jurassic. The flying reptiles of the region have been known since the 18th century. The most famous fossil of all is undoubtedly Archaeopteryx, the bird-reptile of which five examples and a single feather have been found. In addition to reptiles, including Homeosaurus the ancestor of the modern tuatara, one of the early Rhynchocephalians or 'beak heads'. Extensive remains of fish, invertebrates and plants have also been unearthed.

The Bolca deposit
The deposit at Monte Bolca, north of Verona, is the best-known example from the Cenozoic because of the variety and magnificence of the fossils there. The limestone strata, which date back to the Eocene, actually contain the perfectly preserved remains of fish (teleost fish, sharks, skate and eels), crustaceans, various invertebrates and numerous land plants. The abundance of fossil finds at Monte Bolca is probably due to epidemics among the marine fauna caused by the pollution of the waters in the tropical bay existing at that time; this pollution was the result of volcanic eruptions.

The Rancho La Brea deposit
The famous deposit at Rancho La Brea came about as a consequence of a deadly natural trap. The lakes of sticky asphalt there, real oil deposits emerging on the earth's surface, ensnared a large number of animals. These unfortunate creatures stuck fast and died, their remains being preserved in the bitumen. They include quantities of herbivorous mammals, who were possibly running for cover in the lakes while being chased by carnivorous predators. However, the remains of the predators themselves are also plentiful. They include Smilodon, the sabre-toothed tiger, as well as vultures who met their deaths in pursuit of their prey or were drawn there by carrion.

21

The Origin of Life

Life on Earth began over 3,000 million years ago and was for a long time confined to water. Until 700 million years ago, living organisms were microscopic in size, and the sea-bed may have resembled the illustration above, with the most minute bacteria and colonies of microscopic blue–green algae as the predominant forms of life. The photograph shows the remains of one of the first organisms visible to the naked eye. The drawing below gives a schematic idea of the transitions which led procaryote cells to engender eucaryote cells.

The problem of how life arose on Earth has fascinated many scientists. The first was the Russian biochemist A. I. Oparin, who formulated the theory that life originated from a liquid mixture in which the first organic compounds were formed. In an experiment in 1953 which has since become famous, Miller recreated a hypothetical primaeval atmosphere composed of methane, ammonia, hydrogen and water, through which he passed some electrical charges. After a few days amino-acids and other substances, which are the basic components of the living cell, formed in the mixture. Miller's experiment shows that life possibly came about spontaneously, perhaps by means of ultra-violet radiation from the sun rather than electrical energy. The first cells must have been of the simplest type, called procaryotes. Procaryotic cells do not have a distinct nucleus and lack other organelles, such as chloroplasts and mitochondria. These are present and much in evidence in the cells which make up plants and animals, the eucaryotes. Procaryote cells are actually typical of the bacteria and blue-green algae which were therefore likely to have been the first living organisms to appear on Earth. Fossil evidence for the presence of these organisms is so far relatively scarce; but it does seem fairly certain that the first organic matter existed in South African rocks dating back to just over 3,000 million years ago.

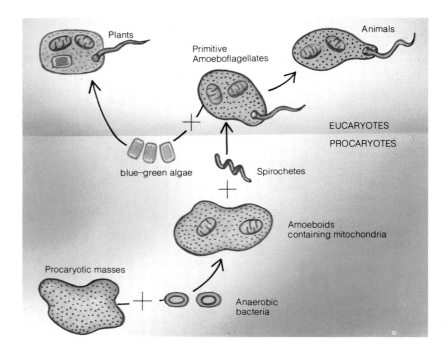

Cells from 2,000 million years ago

Fossil remains of micro-organisms, similar to bacteria and blue–green algae, discovered in rocks in North America which date back about 2,000 million years, clearly show how at that time and probably even earlier organisms made up of cells of the procaryote type had already evolved. However, the most typical and widely found fossil remains of the period preceding the Palaeozoic Era are certainly the stromatoliths: these are remains of colonies of blue–green algae, which had caught up the suspended sediment in the water and so became, as they grew, mineralised structures, varied in form, which could be preserved in the fossil state. These days, stromatoliths are formed particularly in lagoons in Western Australia which have a very high salt water content. The nodules of manganese found in the ocean depths, which represent a very considerable mineral reserve, are also stromatoliths, in this case made out of bacteria. In the drawing below, you can see different types of present-day bacteria.

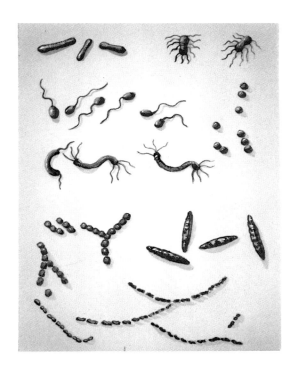

Pre-Palaeozoic fauna
1-2-3-4) Different forms of jellyfish
5) Conomedusites
6-7) Pennatulaceans
8) Spriggina
9-10) Dickinsonia (Annelids)
11-12) Parvancornia (Crustaceans)
13) Praecambridium (Chelicerata)

Evolution of the cell

A crucial stage in the evolution of living things is marked by the transition from the procaryote to the eucaryote cell. There is firm evidence of this transition in Australian rocks going back about 1,000 million years. They contain fossil cells that are clearly eucaryote in type. The eucaryote cells, which reproduce both by mitosis (fission) and by meiosis (sexual reproduction), permit this transition from microscopic to macroscopic life-forms.

The first fossils

Until the 1950s, it was thought that rocks preceding the Cambrian Period contained almost no fossils. However, the amount of evidence on pre-Palaeozoic life has greatly increased since then, and today it appears that for almost the whole of the Phanerozoic, starting from about 3,000 million years ago, life existed all over the Earth in the form of microscopic animals. It was only about 700 million years ago, in fact, that the first animals visible to the naked eye appeared. These were discovered for the first time at Ediacara, in central Southern Australia, in 1949; but their emergence from pre-Cambrian formations was not recognised until

1958. The Ediacara fauna contain organisms a few centimetres in size which have already attained a high degree of diversification. This is a clear sign that there was a previous evolving history about which we still know nothing. Some of the animals are clearly identified because they resemble present-day forms, like the jellyfish (see photo, bottom left) or the worms (photo, centre), this includes animals totally unknown to us, such as the *Tribrachidium* (photo, below), and strange animals shaped like birds' feathers; animals like these have also been found in pre-Cambrian rocks in England, Russia, South Africa and North America.

The Palaeozoic Era

Period	Millions of years ago
PERMIAN	280
CARBONIFEROUS	340
DEVONIAN	395
SILURIAN	435
ORDOVICIAN	500
CAMBRIAN	570

The Primary Era, or Palaeozoic, which in Greek means 'of very early organisms', is the period dating from 570 to 230 million years ago. These 340 million years subdivide into six periods. The oldest was the Cambrian, followed by the Ordovician, Silurian, Devonian, Carboniferous and Permian.

The Palaeozoic was of vital importance in the evolution of life in the seas and on dry land. Several aspects of life in the seas at this time are very interesting, for some weird and complex arthropods lived there. These included the trilobites, now extinct, from which the present-day arthropods later evolved; and the graptolites resembling umbrella spokes, which drifted on the currents. Other animals, resembling present-day lamellibranchs, rested on the sea-bed on their long spines. This was the dawning of the era which saw the disappearance of the early marine vertebrates, the colonising of land above sea-level by the arthropods, and the appearance of the first plants. A major event occurred about 350 million years ago in the Devonian period, when the amphibians, which had derived from crossopterygian fish, emerged onto the land above sea-level. Shortly afterwards, the first reptiles evolved from them.

The Palaeozoic is of great interest, not only biologically but also geographically. The continents which had begun to separate moved closer together and in the Permian, the continental land masses joined in a super-continent. This had major and fatal consequences for the marine and land faunas, for numerous species became extinct.

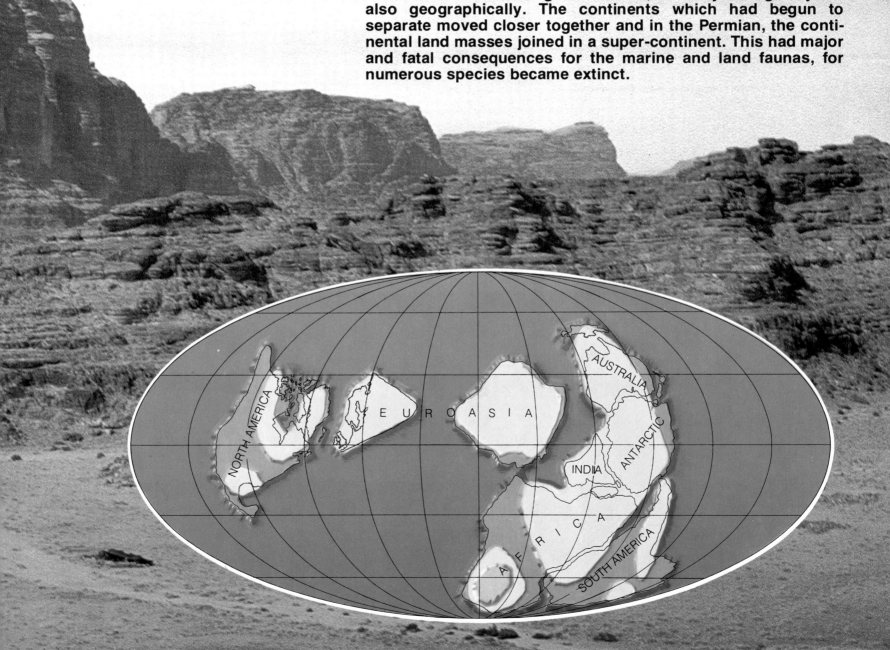

Early marine fauna

The fossil-bearing deposits which belong to the Palaeozoic Era, starting from the Cambrian Period, indicate a marine world inhabited by numerous life-forms. Though primitive, these had already shown a notable level of specialisation and diversification. This possibly suggests an easier process of evolution, but unfortunately only very scanty evidence of it has survived. As early as the Cambrian, we find the radiolaria among the unicellular animals, or protozoans. Radiolaria had a siliceous shell, and foraminifera with their calcareous shell were also present at this time. Foraminifera were more plentiful in the Carboniferous and Permian. Sponges also existed then, together with organisms probably related to them, such as the archaeocyathids. These were of considerable importance in the formation of the first reefs, playing the part which corals took over later. In the same period, the coelenterates had already reached a marked level of evolution, especially the jellyfish, which occur from the pre-Cambrian onwards. The real development of the coelenterates, and in particular of the anthozoans (corals), began with the Silurian. The diffusion of tetracorals, together with the stromatopores and bryozoans, contributed to the formation of the great Palaeozoic coral-producing reefs. The decline of the tetracorals started in the Carboniferous and they became extinct with the end of the Palaeozoic. However, the most widespread animals in the Cambrian seas were probably the brachiopods and above all the trilobites. Brachiopods are animals inside a bivalve shell. They are something like lamellibranch molluscs; but there are considerable differences between the two. Brachiopods existed in a number of already very diversified and specialised forms, and in the Silurian reached the peak of their development. Trilobites undoubtedly represent the most developed forms of life to be found in the Cambrian. They, too, had already developed many differences in form and an advanced state of evolution. The fact that they were preserved in large numbers in rocks was due to their chitinous exoskeleton, which lent itself well to fossilisation.

Early marine fauna
The above photo shows a magnificent example of *Homotelus bromidensis*, a trilobite which lived in North America in the Ordovician Period. The trilobites, a class of arthropods now completely extinct, were very widespread in the Palaeozoic Era.

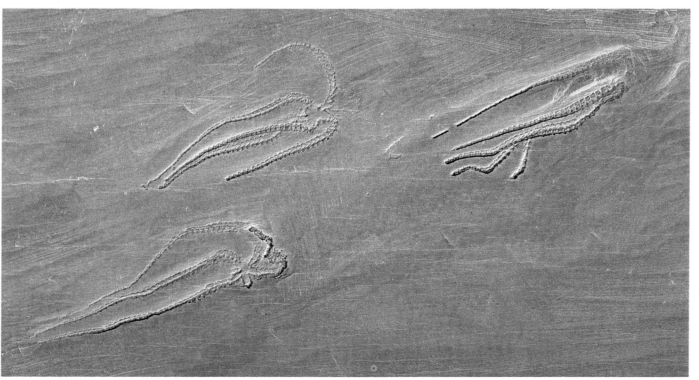

In the seas of the Palaeozoic
The seas of the Cambrian Period already contained bryozoans, gasteropod mollusca and cephalopod mollusca as well as the first nautiloids to have developed tests (or shells). These would flourish in the Silurian. Others with origins in the Cambrian are the graptolites — colonial organisms exclusive to the Palaeozoic. A number of fossil-bearing deposits from this period have provided fossils of invertebrates which are almost devoid of hard parts: from this stems our knowledge of the existence of worms (polychete annelids), chaetognaths, and also onychophoran arthropods. There is no lack, either, of echinoderms, which nowadays comprise sea-urchins, starfish (left) and sea-lilies or crinoids (right).

A Palaeozoic sea bed

The presence of fossil remains of marine animals characterises only those rocks dating back to the start of the Palaeozoic Era. This proves that animal and plant life were then confined to the seas and oceans, but that all the groups of invertebrate animals alive today were already represented. In the Ordovician Period, about 450 million years ago, there appeared the first vertebrates. We are still not sure whether they originated in freshwater or in marine habitats. It was not until the Silurian Period, about 430 million years ago, that living organisms were populating the land above sea-level.

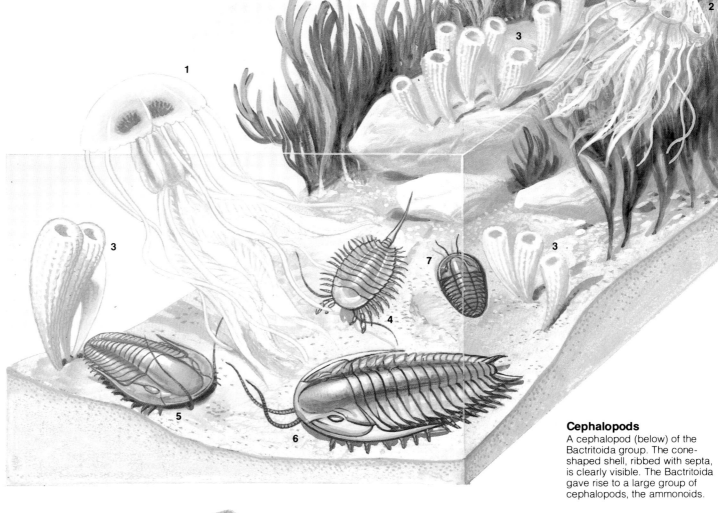

1-2)	Jellyfish
3)	Sponges
4)	Arachnids
5-6-7)	Trilobites (Ogygopsis, Olinoidea, Ellipsocephalus)

Cephalopods

A cephalopod (below) of the Bactritoida group. The cone-shaped shell, ribbed with septa, is clearly visible. The Bactritoida gave rise to a large group of cephalopods, the ammonoids.

Problematic organisms

The rocks of the North American Carboniferous afford numerous examples of invertebrates which inhabited the deltas of big rivers. Besides animals which can clearly be linked to known or still surviving groups, animals have been found here whose precise taxonomic status is still unknown. These include *Tullymonstrum gregarium* (right), a strange creature with a funnel-shaped head. It had two eyes on opposite sides in the middle of the funnel, linked together by a bar.

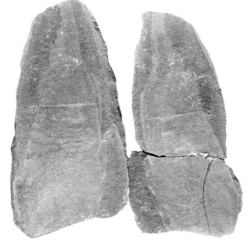

Brachiopods

Brachiopods developed rapidly and were very widespread throughout the Palaeozoic. Below left: a brachiopod of the genus *Spirifer*. Right: a jellyfish.

27

Trilobites and graptolites

Trilobites and graptolites are two groups of animals which were widely diffused during the Palaeozoic, but became extinct before that Era ended. Trilobites are segmented arthropods with many legs. Their name comes from the characteristic division of the body into three parts, longitudinally and across. Lengthwise, a trilobite's body has a head or *cephalon*, a *thorax* made up of a certain number of segments, each divided into three parts by two longitudinal grooves and having two legs; and a posterior section called a pygidium. Trilobites are mostly small-scale creatures, though some forms can be as much as 60–70cms long.

Graptolites are colonial organisms; they lived in a colony and were linked to each other by a branched structure called a stolon. Graptolites lived in the Palaeozoic seas from the Cambrian to the Carboniferous, and belong to the Stomacordata group. This group stands midway between the invertebrates and the vertebrates. Both trilobites and graptolites are very important in the stratigraphy of the Palaeozoic Era.

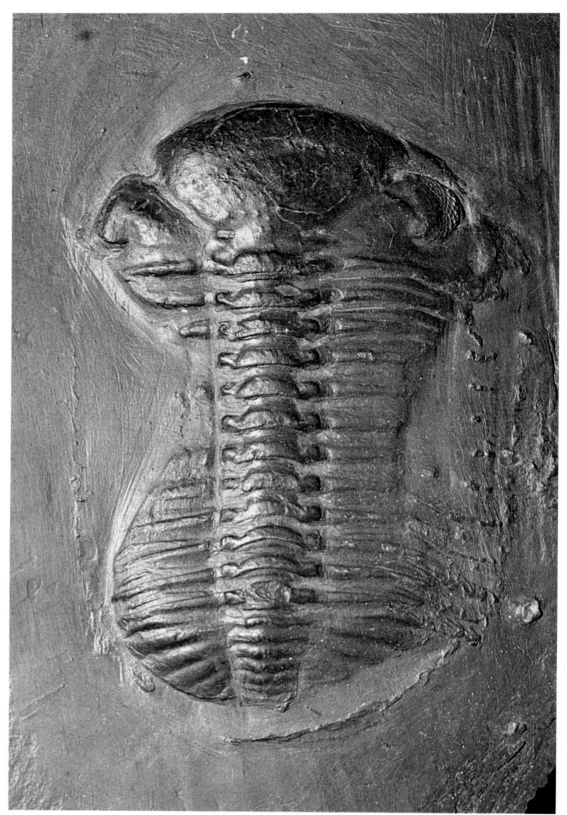

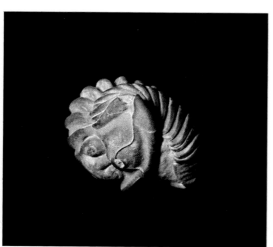

How trilobites lived
A Devonian trilobite of the genus *Phacops* (above) and *Conocoryphe sulzeri*, a trilobite from the Cambrian in Bohemia (above left). Trilobites usually lived on the sea bed, and some species may have been able to swim. A number of trilobites could roll up together into a ball when danger threatened, as shown in the photograph of a *Flexicalymene* (left).

The structure of trilobites
The drawing on the right shows the main subdivisions of a trilobite's carapace. The *cephalon* is divided into three parts: a central part, or glabella, and two side parts, or cheeks, containing the eyes, which are usually composite. The *thorax* is made up of a variable number of segments that could be articulated separately. Each carried a pair of legs. The posterior part, or pygidium, consists of segments joined together and often merged. An idea of the variety of the forms of trilobite can be gleaned from the drawing on the page opposite.

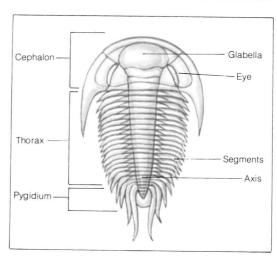

A primaeval sea bed

The illustration reconstructs the sea bed as it might have looked in the distant past; the animals represented were not contemporary. They lived at different times during the Lower Palaeozoic. They include a *Ctenopyge*, a trilobite which lived in the Cambrian and had a grotesque appearance because of its long spinate apophyses. Other trilobites from the same period also on the sea bed, are *Paradoxides* and *Solenopleura*, both very similar in form. Also typical of the Cambrian Period are the small *Agnostus*, whose cephalon is the same size as its pygidium, and *Bailiella* and *Rusophycus*, the latter sunk into the soft mud of the sea bed. Colonies of graptolites are floating in the water: *Dictyonema*, a typical Cambrian graptolite, and two forms that lived in the Silurian, *Pristiograptus* and *Cyrtograptus*, and have a distinctive spiral shape. The two nautiloids with developed 'tests' lived during the Ordovician Period.

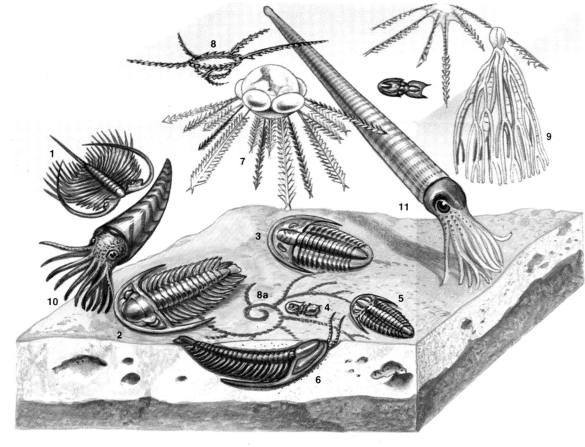

TRILOBITES
1) Ctenopyge
2) Paradoxides
3) Solenopleura
4) Agnostus
5) Bailiella
6) Rusophycus

GRAPTOLITES
7–7a) Pristiograptus
8–8a) Cyrtograptus
9) Dictyonema

NAUTILOIDS
10) Orthoceras
11) Long-coned Orthoceras

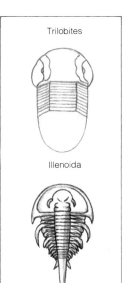

Trilobites

Illenoida

Ptychoparia Strata

Trinucleus

Phacops

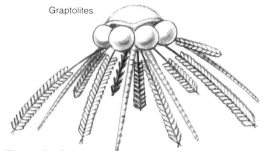

Graptolites

The colonies
Some graptolites (benthos) were attached to the sea bed, while others were suspended in the sea at the mercy of the currents (planktonic and epiplanktonic). Above: a colony of graptolites of the genus *Diplograptus*.

Graptolites
Graptolites were exclusively colonial marine animals: each individual creature lived inside a chitinous shell (or theca) linked to the other individuals in the colony by a chord or stolon. Some of them formed colonies patterned like branches. Others joined together in shapes resembling a wood-saw. Appearing first in the Middle Cambrian, graptolites became widespread, especially in the Ordovician and Silurian: they became extinct after that in the Lower Carboniferous. Graptolites are of great importance in the stratigraphy of Palaeozoic rocks, in particular those of the Ordovician and Silurian; the distribution area they cover is so large and their forms evolved so fast that the presence of graptolite remains enables rocks a long way apart to be correlated.

Taxonomic position
Graptolites, when found, have usually been deformed by being crushed between schists and slates; so, for a long time their exact taxonomic position remained in doubt. The result was that they were originally classified among the coelenterates (which comprise corals and jellyfish). However, it has been possible to analyse specimens preserved in limestones and sandstones which suffered no deformation. When isolated by the use of hydrochloric and hydrofluoric acid (above and right) their overall structure can be studied. Consequently, they have been classified with the Stomochordata.

Structure of graptolites
Detailed studies on graptolite structure have shown that the way these animals were organised was very similar to that of a living pterobranch, the *Rhabdopleura*. Pterobranchs, like other Stomochordata, are not very widely dispersed animals and possess a number of characteristics, such as a dorsal nervous sytem, similar to vertebrates. So, graptolites, too, come to occupy a taxonomic position midway between invertebrates and vertebrates.

Left: a detail of a colony of graptolites magnified many times. Right: also greatly enlarged, a detail from a colony of *Rhabdopleura*, a living pterobranch.

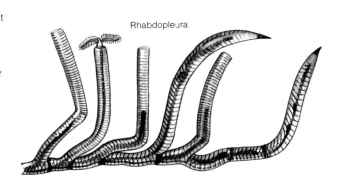

Rhabdopleura

Palaeozoic reefs

A reef consists of a rich conglomeration of animals and plants; these help construct their own environment, a habitat which in topographical terms has risen from the sea bed and is in effect an elevation. Present-day bioconstructed reefs, whose mineral composition is provided by living organisms, are typical of tropical waters and are found throughout the world. Most typical are the atolls and the Great Coral Barrier Reef in Australia. Among the biggest contributory organisms in the present reefs are calcareous algae of various types, especially corals. Other invertebrates are involved but to a lesser extent. About nine-tenths of a reef is made up of fine sandy detritus which mostly consists of the remains of hard parts (shells etc.) of the animals living on it; this detritus is retained and incorporated by the algae, and subsequently turned into limestone. A reef is an environment very rich in life, the sea equivalent of tropical forests, and the organisms represented there belong to almost all the animal *phyla*. As well as the algae and corals already mentioned, sponges, protozoans, bryozoans, echinoderms, brachiopods and mollusca all flourish there and help build up the reef. Conversely, worms, crustaceans and fish, though abundant, do not play a significant part, since their remains are systematically destroyed by other organisms. The formation of a reef requires an even all year round temperature — no great fluctuations between seasons and no temperatures below 20° Centigrade: this explains why reefs grow up along tropical belts; the depth of the sea around a reef is not usually greater than 60 metres. Reefs began to form in the pre-Cambrian with the formation of stromatoliths, or reefs made exclusively of algae. In the course of time, different groups of animals in turn played leading roles in building up the reefs.

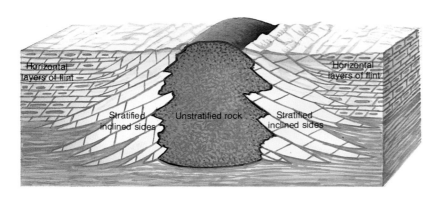

The first reefs

The first proper reef 'communities' appeared in the Cambrian Period, which saw the start of a widespread diffusion of animals with calcareous skeletons. Archaeocyathids, which lived in the Cambrian, were the first organisms to be united with the algae in the building of reefs. In the Ordovician, the bryozoans, which were colonial organisms secreting a calcareous skeleton, took on a particularly important role as reef-builder organisms; so did stromatoporoids, and also the first corals, the so-called tabulate corals, and tetracorals (left). The geological sketch (above left) is a schematic section of a North American Palaeozoic reef; it shows the reef's unstratified rock, rich in organic detritus, and its stratified inclined sides, while horizontal calcareous layers with nodules of flint are formed between one reef and the next.

The big builders

Shortly after the appearance of the tabulate corals, another important group of corals arose in the Ordovician: the important tetracorals or rugose corals, which enjoyed considerable diffusion until the Middle Carboniferous. Together with the bryozoans, stromatoporoids and corallinaceous red algae, they played a major part in the building of reefs. From the Carboniferous until the end of the Palaeozoic, as the diffusion of corals declined, a more significant role was taken on by the crinoids. This group of echinoderms possessed an external skeleton composed of different sets of plates and lived attached to the sea-bed by a stalk. Remains of crinoids were in some cases the main component of rocks, as in the case of reefs in the British Carboniferous. Brachiopods were also very widely diffused in the Upper Palaeozoic, as demonstrated by the numerous genuses found in rocks of that period: among them was *Richtofenia* (above). In the Upper Palaeozoic two groups of green algae were also quite important: the Codiaceae and the Dasycladiaceae.

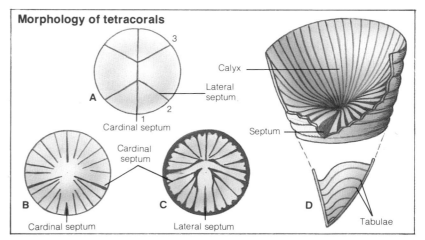

Morphology of tetracorals

A reef community from the North American Carboniferous

Between the Devonian and Carboniferous Periods, there was a crisis in the reef communities: the tabulate corals and stromatoporoids had reached a critical point, while sponges, crinoids, bryozoans and brachiopods were becoming more and more important.

1-2) Echinoderms (Crinoids and starfish)
3) Bryozoans (Archimedes)
4) Ammonites
5-6) Brachiopods
7) Coelenterates (Tetracorals)
8) Calcareous sponges

Morphology of tetracorals

The schematic diagram (left) shows the inside of a tetracoral and its stages of growth. In a coral the single polyp secretes a cone-shaped or cylindrical calcareous skeleton divided inside by horizontal walls (tabulae) and vertical walls (septa). In the calyx of a tetracoral, the septa were arranged in a particular way, lining up as they formed around four lateral septa (A 2-3) branching out from a principal septum (A 1); the part of this septum from which the first pair of lateral septa branch off is called a cardinal septum. The opposite part is a ventral septum. A and B show early and advanced stages in a solitary tetracoral's growth; C and D show the lower and upper parts of a *Zaphrentites* tetracoral in cross-section.

Tetracorals

Calceola sandalina (above) is a typical solitary tetracoral of the Devonian Period. Like other tetracorals, *Calceola* had an operculum on its upper part.

Bryozoans

Archimedes, a Carboniferous bryozoan (left), used to form colonies in the shape of superimposed funnels, which imparted its characteristic helicoidal appearance.

Corals

The name *corals* usually refers to a group of coelenterates existing in a single polyp stage fixed to the sea bed and secreting an internal calcareous skeleton. They are currently the main builders of reefs. The hexacorals are recorded from the Triassic onwards, whereas the tabulate corals and tetracorals, or rugose corals, are exclusive to the Palaeozoic. Tetracorals (right) occur in both colonial and solitary forms, the latter being sometimes on a giant scale — more than 15cms in diameter and a metre in length.

Tabulate corals

Halisites (above) was a tabulate coral which formed skeletons that were ellipsoidal in section, and were attached in such a way that in profile they looked like entangled chains. The tabulate corals were distinguished by barely developed septa and an inside divided up into horizontal tabulae.

Life comes to land

The colonisation of land above sea level by living organisms is believed to have started in the Upper Silurian, about 420 million years ago. Previously, life had been entirely confined to the waters: The first micro-organisms had appeared in an aquatic habitat. More complex life-forms had later developed in the water, when water already contained all the animal *phyla* that still survive to this day. It was in the sea that the first vertebrates, the agnatha, made their appearance in the Ordovician, as did the first vertebrates with jaw-bones, the fish Acanthodii, in the following Silurian Period. In contrast with the teeming life of the waters, the land above sea level was deserted and bereft of life in a fashion which has no equivalent on Earth today. No life-form had developed on land for millions of years. This underlines the importance of the step taken by the earliest plants to colonise the banks and river basins. The difficulties facing a transition from aquatic to subaereal environment were enormous. In general an aquatic habitat offered more stable environmental conditions, with smaller fluctuations in temperature and light. Furthermore, organisms did not need structures to help their bodies withstand the force of gravity, nor systems for the retention of liquids to avoid becoming dehydrated. It was by overcoming these and other difficulties that psilophytal plants were able to make their appearance on dry land.

Earliest subaereal life-forms

Only a few animal *phyla* have so far managed to adapt themselves, at least in a number of forms, to the difficulties which a subaereal life environment entails. Among them are the chordates (which means mainly vertebrates), the annelids (earthworms), the mollusca (gasteropods), and the arthropods (insects etc.). Judging by the fossil remains found in Wales and the Island of Gotland and dating back to the Upper Silurian, arthropods were the first animals to appear on dry land. These were myriapods and forms similar to early scorpions. Only the earliest plants had preceded them in the colonisation of the subaereal habitat, as shown by the sequence of illustrations below. The first two pictures depict two successive phases of the Silurian Period: the appearance of plants is followed by the

appearance of the first terrestrial arthropods. The third picture relates to the Devonian Period during which the first terrestrial vertebrates, the amphibians, came on the scene. The illustration shows *Eusthenopteron*, a fish with characteristics midway between fish and amphibians, and *Ichthyostega*, a very primitive amphibian but one already able to move and breathe in a subaereal habitat. The above photo shows the fossil print of an amphibian similar to *Seymouria*, an evolved amphibian which has characteristics in keeping with transition into the reptile class. Reptiles were the first vertebrates which managed to leave behind the aquatic environment for the laying of eggs and the development of embryos, thus opening the way to the colonisation of the subaereal habitat by vertebrates.

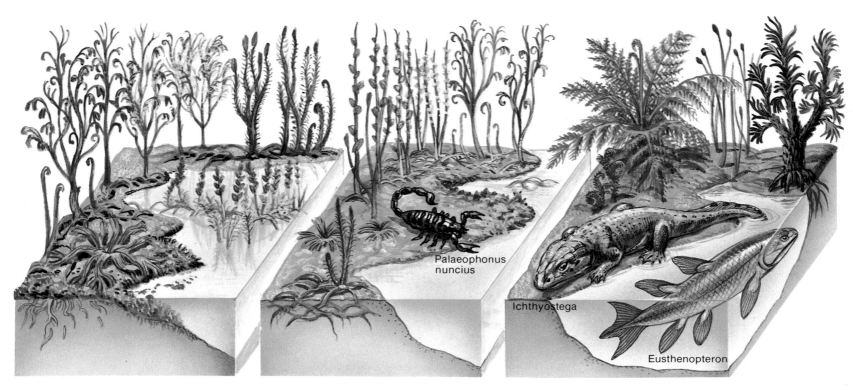

Palaeophonus nuncius

Ichthyostega

Eusthenopteron

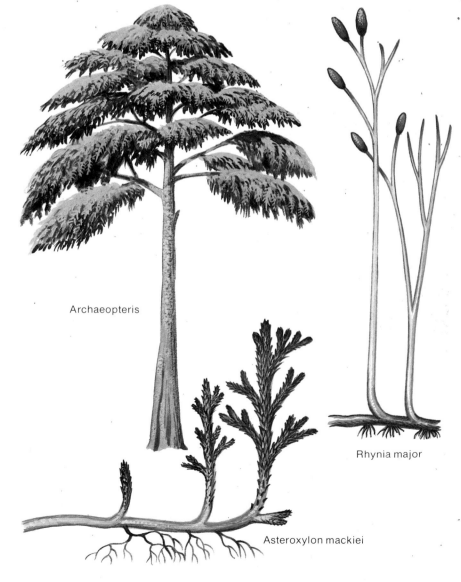

A landscape in the Devonian

Towards the start of the Devonian, the general outline of lagoons and coastal pools must have looked very similar to the reconstruction in the drawing (right). A low level of vegetation already growing on the banks, was made up of primitive psilophytal plants, the oldest vascular form of plant life. Here there existed plants belonging to the genuses *Protolepidodendron* (1) which had a stem reaching 15mm in diameter, and bifurcated leaves arranged in a spiral; *Psilophyton* (2) which had a leafless stem with spiniform bristles sprouting at random; and *Sciadophyton* (3), a small leafless plant which developed with radial shoots.

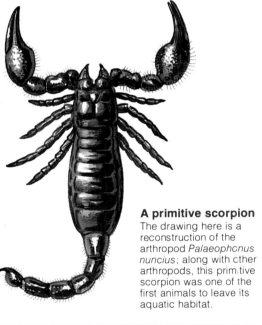

A primitive scorpion

The drawing here is a reconstruction of the arthropod *Palaeophcnus nuncius*; along with cther arthropods, this primtive scorpion was one of the first animals to leave its aquatic habitat.

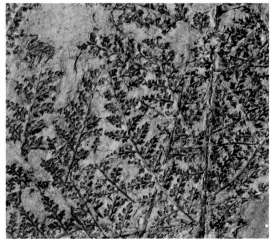

The first vascular plants

Vascular plants, or tracheophytes, have a circulatory system consisting of vessels which bring juices from the earth into the different parts of the body of the plant, and are thus adapted to life in a subaereal setting. They usually have ligneous roots, stem, leaves and tissues. The origin of vascular plants is still not certain: the oldest known examples belonged to the psilophytals, of which there are only a few forms still extant. The psilophytal plants were particularly widespread during the Devonian Period, although the oldest forms date back to the Upper Silurian. They did not have roots in the true sense: that function was performed by the stalk beneath the surface. The drawings (right) are reconstructions of two psilophytal plants: *Rhynia*, from the Devonian, without leaves, and *Asteroxylon*, with aereal stalks bearing small leaves. Primitive ferns like *Archaeopteris* (right) existed as early as the Devonian: together with lycopods and horsetails, these would be predominant in the forests of the Carboniferous. The photograph (left) is of a Carboniferous fern.

Archaeopteris

Rhynia major

Asteroxylon mackiei

The first vertebrates

Vertebrates comprise all those animals which have an internal skeleton made up of different bones, i.e. fish, amphibians, reptiles, birds, and mammals. They made their appearance in the Ordovician. It is in this period that we find the first, though incomplete, remains which undoubtedly belong to vertebrates. Very little is known as yet about the habits and exact morphology of these primitive vertebrates. Nevertheless, we do know for certain that they were Agnatha, the fish without jawbones, to which belong the remains of vertebrates that existed in the Ordovician and in most of the Silurian. It was from this group that present-day cyclostomes (lampreys) derived. The primitive agnatha were very unusual animals: often rather small in size, about thirty centimetres on average, they were generally covered by numerous bony plates. Thanks to these plates, which have been preserved in sedimentary rocks, we can identify these fish: their skeleton, made of cartilage like that of modern sharks, and not of real calcified bone, had little chance of being fossilised. Because of the absence of jawbones, it is most unlikely that these fish fed off other animals or aquatic plants. However, from the shape of the skeleton and their skull, it seems that most of them had adapted to living on the muddy sea beds, combing the sediments in search of organic particles on which they fed. There were also swimming forms, feeding on plankton suspended in the water, although their aptitude for swimming was minimal, for they lacked the proper paired fins possessed by more evolved fish. The Agnatha were never very widespread, and they went through a period of rapid decline from the Devonian onwards, alongside the diffusion of the first fish to have jawbones, the Placoderms.

Origin of the vertebrates

The origin of vertebrates is a problem which has not yet been completely solved. Nonetheless, there are animals with characteristics midway between invertebrates and vertebrates. These have a central 'chord' or notochord of a gelatinous organic material, as in the embryos of vertebrates. These animals, which are grouped as Cephalocordata (or Lancelets), like the amphioxus, have left few fossil remains that could serve to document their evolution. This is due to their lack of hard parts that could be preserved. By comparing their differences of structure, it is, however, possible to obtain an idea of the evolutionary pattern that led up to the vertebrates: the drawing (left) illustrates one of the probable patterns of evolution this intermediary group of animals underwent, which has them originating from a hypothetical sessile filtrator animal.

Gemuendina stuertzi (above); a placoderm from the Devonian.

Primitive filtrator vertebrate

Amphioxus (or Lancelet)

Evolved chordates

Tunicates

Ancestral tunicates with swimming larvae

Worms

Primitive echinoderms

Pterobranchs

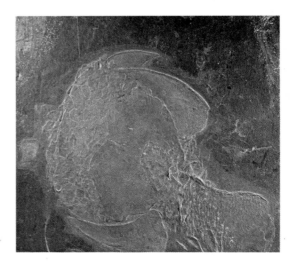

Evolution of the vertebrates

According to one of the latest theories, the evolutionary journey towards the vertebrates passed through the Echinoderm group, meaning the exclusively Palaeozoic group of Eleutherozoa, which were widespread from the Cambrian to the Devonian. A number of larval forms of echinoderm are very similar to those of worm-shaped animals equipped with a stomachord, the anlage of a notochord, comprising the still-living Balanoglossus and the extinct graptolites. One step further on from these stomochordata are the tunicates, the ascidians, and subsequently the *Cephalochordata*. All these groups possessed characteristics increasingly close to the vertebrate group. This suggests, even in the absence of fossil evidence, that the first vertebrates, the fish Agnatha, evolved through animals of this type. The photo is of Drepanaspis, an Agnatha from the Devonian.

A sea in the Devonian

The drawing (right) is a reconstruction of a Devonian seascape, showing fish of the type without mandibles and another, more evolved type with mandibles. The fish Agnatha are easily distinguished by the carapace in the cephalic area — unusual in fish which had jawbones, except for the placoderms. On the sea bed are *Cephalaspis* and *Drepanaspis*, both forms adapted to living on muddy sea beds, while *Pteraspis* and *Hemicyclaspis* were more adapted to active swimming. *Climatius*, an Acanthodian fish with a jawbone and a shape like a shark, swims in search of prey.

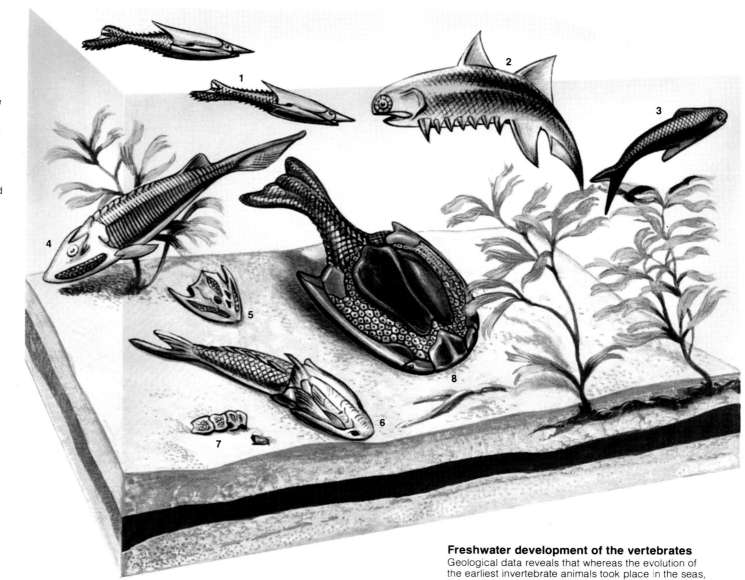

1 Pteraspis
2 Climatius
3 Thelodus
4 Hemicyclaspis
5 Cephalaspis
6 Pteraspis
7 Eurypterus
8 Drepanaspis

Giant crustaceans

Crustaceans of extraordinary appearance lived in the seas of the Palaeozoic Era, and are today classified as Giant Water Scorpions. This class of arthropod gave rise to spectacular forms. Some grew to great size, above three metres long. They had strong claws and are believed to have been active predators of primitive fish with jawbones. However, fossil evidence indicates that they were, in their turn, the prey of more evolved fish which *did* have jawbones. The Giant Water Scorpions (below is an example of a eurypterid) are regarded as the direct antecedents of the first arthropods which inhabited dry land, in particular the scorpions.

Freshwater development of the vertebrates

Geological data reveals that whereas the evolution of the earliest invertebrate animals took place in the seas, the evolution of the vertebrates, from the Ordovician Period into the Devonian, occurred to a large extent in fresh or brackish waters after developing initially in a marine habitat primitive fish evolved in great basins like lakes, or in delta areas where river waters became mixed with saline sea water. The picture below shows an example of *Pterychthyodes*, belonging to a group of fish, the placoderms, which were among the first vertebrates to have jawbones.

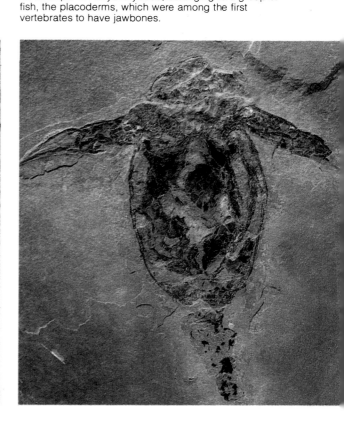

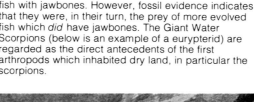

35

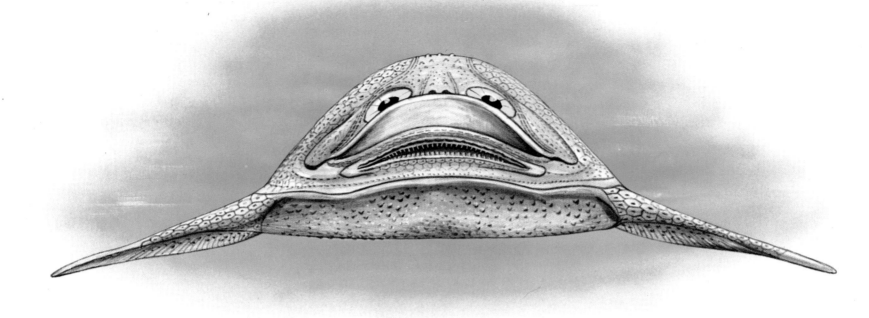

Armoured fish

In the Upper Silurian, an important event in the history of the vertebrates took place: the first fish to have real jawbones, the Acanthodii, made their appearance. These were fish resembling sharks, with large bones reinforcing each flipper. They had big eyes and small olfactory organs, and they were especially voracious and active predators, unlike the contemporary Agnatha fish who were used to being limivorous. The acquisition of real jawbones, and with that, increased feeding possibilities, enabled the Acathodii to occupy a large number of the ecological niches denied to primitive fish. The latter, not having jawbones, had limited chances of development, and went no further than specialised forms which could filter the mud on the sea bed or were adapted to a parasitic way of life as is still led today by lampreys. The development of jawbones, however, led to an enormously increased capacity for searching out and eating food, with all the adaptations that followed from that. Among the first fish to have jawbones, the subclass which developed the most spectacular forms was the placoderm.

Widespread from the Devonian Period on but extinct during the Carboniferous that followed, the placoderms are better known as 'armoured fish' because of the curious carapaces made of bony plates which in various forms covered the front part of the body.

Curious forms
One particularly curious group of placoderm fish is the stegoselachians. Their outward appearance resembled present-day types of ray, like *Gemuendina* (above: front view; below: dorsal view). *Gemuendina* was a characteristically flat fish; it had a very broad head and a tapering body, with a pair of very extended pectoral fins which gave it a look typical of present day skate; *Gemuendina* lived exclusively in the Devonian.

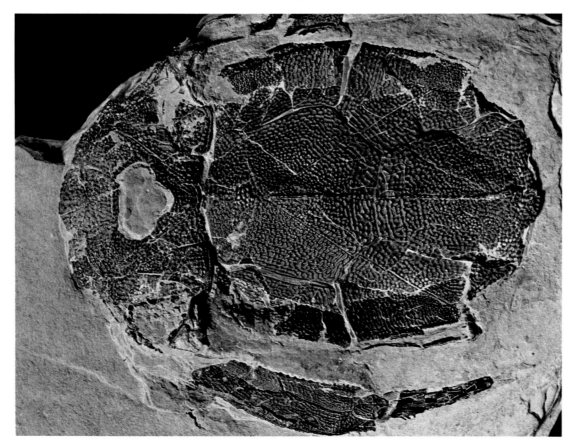

Placoderms
Placoderms probably derived from the Agnatha fish, and are virtually exclusive to the Devonian period. They probably gave rise to chondrites, the first cartilaginous fish like modern sharks, and to osteichthyes, fish with an ossified skeleton. The name 'placoderms' has to do with the presence, in a number of forms, of complex dermal armour-plating on the head and over the front part of the body. This is reminiscent of the most primitive ostracoderm agnatha, though placoderms differ by being made up, not of continuous plates, but of smaller, more numerous ones. The rest of the body could have been covered by scales or may have been naked, as in the case of *Bothriolepis*. The carapace of Bothriolepis is shown left, together with two armoured pectoral appendices.

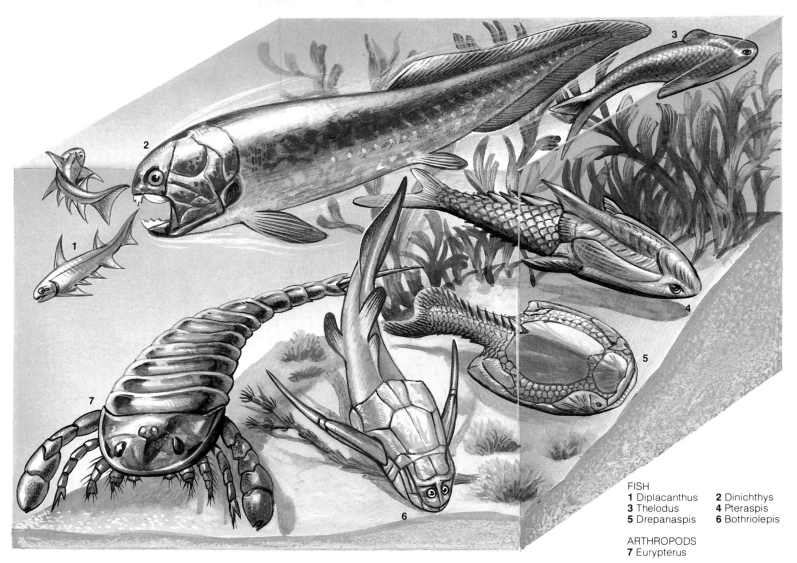

FISH
1 Diplacanthus **2** Dinichthys
3 Thelodus **4** Pteraspis
5 Drepanaspis **6** Bothriolepis

ARTHROPODS
7 Eurypterus

In the seas of the Palaeozoic

The reconstruction of a Palaeozoic seascape (above): in addition to a crustacean of the Giant Water Scorpion type, there are a number of forms of Agnatha fish and a *Bothriolepis*, which lived on the sea bed, while fish of an already more evolved type are shown actively swimming. The two shark-shaped fish with spikes on their fins are Acanthodii, an exclusively Palaeozoic group of which very little is known. The bigger fish is a *Dinichthys*.

Primitive fish

The schematic drawing below shows the probable phylogeny of primitive fish. On the left are the groups still living today, like lampreys, sharks, dipnoans and the latimeria, which is the sole survivor of the coelacanths. The evolution of the ostracoderms led, by way of the placoderms, to two important groups of bony fish: actinopterygians, from which modern fish evolved, and the crossopterygians, precursors of the first vertebrates to inhabit dry land, the amphibians.

A placoderm from North America

Bothriolepis is a small placoderm which lived in North America in the Upper Devonian; the largest specimens measured as much as 30cms. They had eyes close together on the back of the head, with nostrils between them. The mouth was on the underside. Such a combination suggests that *Bothriolepis* lived on lake beds, in the same way as the ostracoderm, whose form it resembles. The drawings show the outline of the carapace seen from above (a) and underneath (b).

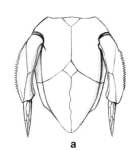

a

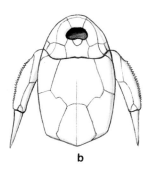

b

Phylogeny of primitive fish

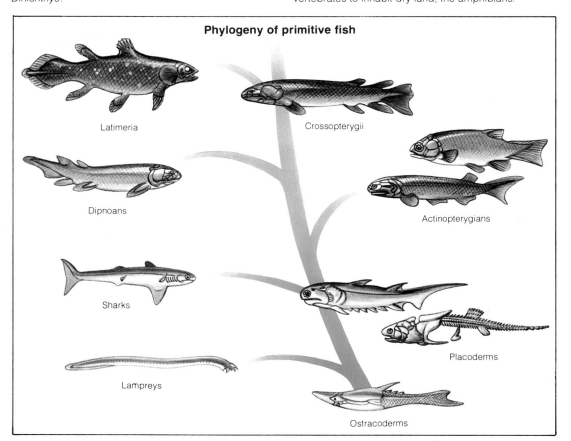

Latimeria

Crossopterygii

Actinopterygians

Dipnoans

Sharks

Placoderms

Lampreys

Ostracoderms

A predator from the seas of the Devonian

The real ruler of the seas in the Upper Devonian was *Dinichthys* (right), which could grow to a length of ten metres. It had strong jawbones fitted with broad cutting plates which made it a most formidable predator.

37

The origin of the amphibians

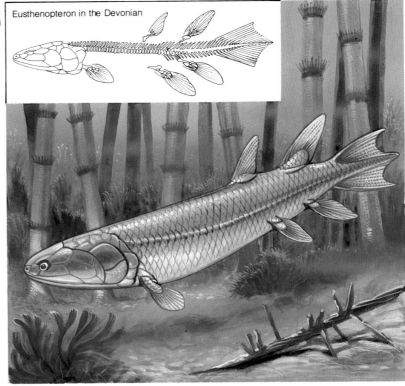

Eusthenopteron in the Devonian

The appearance of the first vertebrates on dry land was possibly due to a series of geographic and climatic changes which proved decisive. As a consequence, a group of fish which had been living in freshwater basins evolved forms with limbs, and were able to breathe air. These were the first amphibians. In the Devonian, after the period of mountain formation known as the Caledonian orogeny, a continental type of climate set in over the land above sea level, with very marked fluctuations in daily and seasonal temperatures. Water levels in the rivers and freshwater basins were subjected to wide variations, and at times they dried up completely. In basins where the water level was going down, asphyxial conditions were created by the excessive crowding together of living organisms; this caused widespread epidemics among animals, whose carcasses helped to aggravate environmental problems. In such situations, the survivors were animals able to breathe in oxygen not only from water but also, when necessary, from air, and capable of moving over dry land in search of basins where conditions were more favourable. This sort of adaptation is the one practised today by the dipnoans. These fish equipped with lungs, which live in Africa, Australia and South America, bury themselves in the mud during droughts and live in a cocoon made out of mucus secreted by their skin, waiting for the water to return. The first amphibians, however, originated from another group of fish, the rhipidistians, which were related to the present-day coelacanth *Latimeria*. They possessed fins that could move on land as well as in water and lungs derived from the swimming bladder. Their oldest representative is Ichthyostega, an animal whose characteristics combined those of fish and amphibians. Paradoxically, as we have seen, vertebrates learned to live out of the water so that they could also continue to live in the water.

From fish to amphibian

The comparison between the structure of a Devonian fish, *Eusthenopteron* (above) and that of amphibians has made it possible to establish that amphibians derive from crossopterygian fish of the rhipidistian group. The skeleton of *Ichthyostega*, a primitive amphibian, and of *Eusthenopteron* actually contain many similarities; they have the same arrangement of cranial bones, the only difference being that *Ichthyostega*'s parietal bones are underdeveloped and the opercular bones have disappeared. The structure of the vertebrae is also analogous, made up of the neural arch, developed intercentre and reduced pleurocentre. The form of the limbs is also very similar. Although more developed in the amphibian, they are already very complex in fish like *Eusthenopteron*, in which it is already possible to distinguish the typical bones in the limbs of tetrapods. Similarities and differences are shown in the schematic drawing below, which compares a number of details from *Eusthenopteron*, *Ichthyostega*, and from *Eryops*, an amphibian proper.

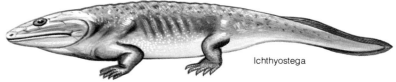

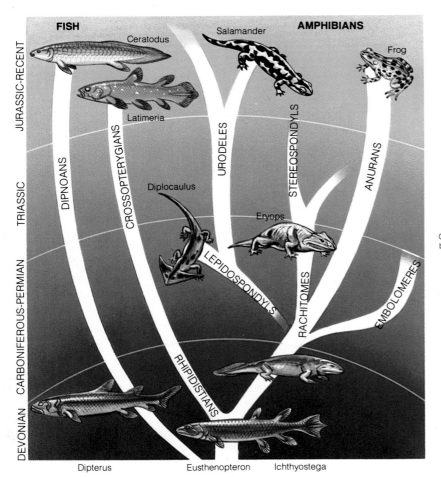

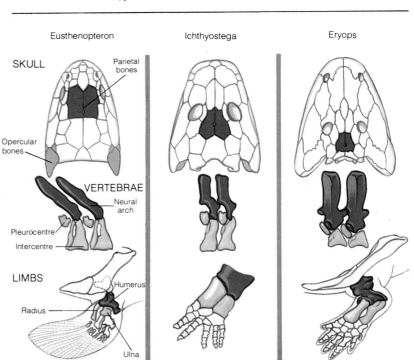

Rhipidistians

Because of the characteristics of their skeletal structure, the crossopterygian fish of the rhipidistian group are thought to be the direct progenitors of amphibians. Palaeontologists were persuaded to accept this theory by the discovery that these fish possessed a choana, an aperture linking the nostrils with the throat. The choana is a characteristic lacking in tetrapods, and no other fish apart from the rhipidistians has it. The photograph (left) is of a primitive rhipidistian, *Gyroptychius*, from the Scottish Devonian.

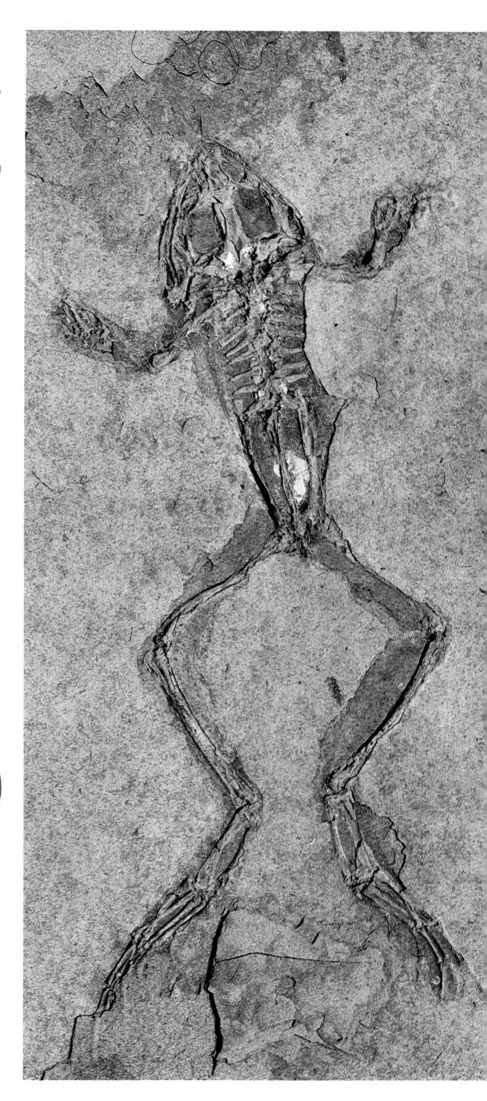

The labyrinthodont tooth

Further evidence that amphibians derived from crossopterygian fish is provided by a characteristic formation of teeth, both in crossopterygians and in many primitive amphibians. Here, in fact, the typical cone-shaped teeth, if looked at in section, show a complex labyrinthine pattern (left). From this comes the name 'labyrinthodont' referring to the teeth. This particular type of formation is due to the number of introflections of two substances making up the teeth: enamel and dentine.

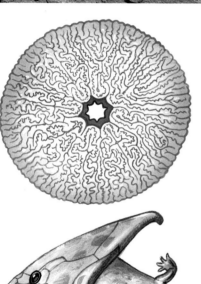

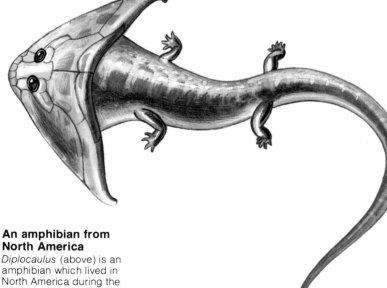

An amphibian from North America

Diplocaulus (above) is an amphibian which lived in North America during the Lower Carboniferous and the Upper Permian. Its very curious head is triangular because of the elongation backwards and sideways of a number of bones in the skull. About 60cms long, it had small limbs with four toes on its front feet and five on its back feet. A bad swimmer, it lived on the beds of basins and fed on plants and insects.

Diffusion of the amphibians

Amphibians had a remarkable diffusion during the Upper Palaeozoic, giving rise to a number of groups. The last amphibians of the labyrinthodont group, which disappeared between the Permian and the Triassic, include the largest amphibians which ever lived, including Mastodon, from the European Triassic; the skull of Mastodon alone measured more than a metre. The labyrinthodonts belong to the aspidospondyl amphibians, whose vertebrae went through a cartilaginous stage before ossifying; modern frogs and toads belong to this group. The photograph (right) is of a frog from the Spanish Tertiary.

Ferns

The pteridophytes predominated in the carboniferous forests. They incorporated groups which today have completely disappeared, like the psilophytes, or groups still in existence though with a much reduced diffusion, such as ferns. Above: a carboniferous fern.

Ferns could be found in a large number of species; their fronds recall those of present-day ferns, but there were also tree-like ferns. Left: a reconstruction of *Neuropteris heterophylla*.

Carboniferous forests

Plants began to colonise dry land from the Upper Silurian onwards. First came a group of pteridophytes, the psilophytes. These plants of modest size consisted of an underground stem, with no roots, which then gave rise to vertical aereal stems. In the Devonian, while the psilophytes were becoming extinct, other pteridophytes appeared: lycopods, horsetails and ferns went to form the first forests. It was in the ensuing period that the forests achieved really massive growth. During the Carboniferous, important geological events took

Pteridophytes

The group of pteridophytes which played a major part in the formation of coal deposits were firstly lycopods like *Sigillaria* and *Lepidodendron*, which could grow as high as 30 metres and had a stem covered in leaves which left distinctive cicatrices when they dropped. Secondly, there were the sphenopods, like *Calamites* (left) of which only the genus *Equisetum* survives.

The map (right) shows the main carboniferous deposits in the world.

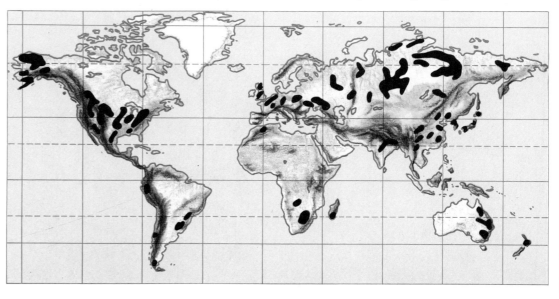

The forests

The reconstruction (left) illustrates a prolific carboniferous forest. A great variety of plants is present, among them cordaites (1), sigillarae (2), lepidodendra (3), horsetails (4), ferns (5), lycopods (6), *Calamites* (7), and tree-like ferns (8). The insect flying on the left is the typical giant dragonfly *Meganeura*, which was capable of a 70cm wing-span.

The enormous diffusion of forests in the Upper Carboniferous led to the formation, during this period, of a sizeable proportion of the world's carbon deposits. These deposits have been extremely important as a source of energy in the rise and development of the industrial age. They are exploited either by opening up underground tunnels or by surface quarrying, as in the photo below.

place which have been named the Variscan or Hercynian orogenic cycle, and led to the formation of mountain chains in North Africa, Europe and North America. In the Mississippian (the first of the two periods into which American geologists divide the Carboniferous), extensive seas covered the continental shields; the climate was variable, and there were rainy regions, dry regions and cold regions with accompanying glaciations. After the Mississippian came the Pennsylvanian, which coincided with the receding of the seas and a variation of the climate which turned humid and warm. Large tropical forests and vast marshes partially covered the continents and in this luxuriant vegetation life on dry land was able to make real progress: numerous fossil remains indicate how varied and diffused life on dry land had already become by that time. The invertebrates known to us include arachnids, myriapods, and insects, beside lamellibranchs and freshwater crustaceans. A large number of small-scale amphibians lived in the marshes, and it was from a group of these, the labyrinthodonts, that the first reptiles evolved in the Carboniferous. The forests also comprised an exceptional variety of plants. Among the pteridophytes, the lycopods and sphenopods grew as high as thirty metres, while ferns also attained giant dimensions. There was an abundance of pteridosperms (cordaites, gingkos) and the cycad gymnosperms, the first advanced plants with seeds.

Carboniferous deposits

The forming of deposits of coal is shown schematically in the drawing (left) in a coastal zone that is sinking, a river delta deposits sediments (clays and sands); on the plain thus formed, a forest grows up which deposits layers of fossil carbons. Subsequently, the sea reinvades the dry land, triggering off a new cycle. The succession of rocks produced in this way (illustrated right), is found in deposits throughout the world.

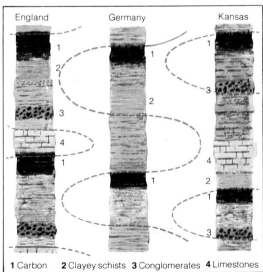

England Germany Kansas

1 Carbon **2** Clayey schists **3** Conglomerates **4** Limestones

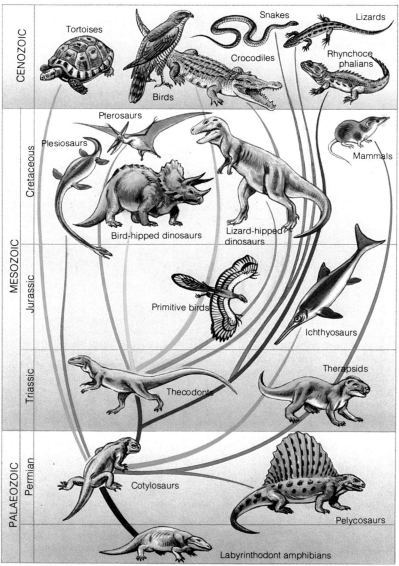

Origin of the reptiles

In the Carboniferous Period, a development occurred which opened the way once and for all for the vertebrates to establish themselves on the huge spaces on dry land which were available to the first animals who could permanently detach themselves from their aquatic environment. There were two important reasons why this had not been possible for the amphibians who were tied to the aquatic habitat. The first was their reproductive habits: amphibians' eggs had to be laid in water. The second was survival: amphibians lacked a waterproof skin and so quickly became dehydrated. In addition, amphibians generally moved better in the water than on *terra firma*. Nevertheless, in the Carboniferous one group of labyrinthodont amphibians gave rise to animals that were able to lay an amniotic egg. This allowed the embryo to grow and develop out of water as well as in, and this resulted in the first reptiles. Reptiles develop directly from the egg and do not pass through a larval stage nor do they possess gills at any period in their life. They also have a horny epidermis often consisting of scales. Even the most primitive reptiles had limbs which functioned better on dry land than those of the labyrinthodont amphibians.

The first reptiles

The first reptiles were the cotylosaurs. They appeared in the Upper Carboniferous and retained several characteristics of the labyrinthodont amphibians. One was a compact type of skull with no temporal apertures like that of modern tortoises. Tortoises derive directly from these early reptiles. Other reptiles evolved in turn from the cotylosaurs, shown in the diagram (left). Below: *Labidosaurus*, a cotylosaur from the Permian.

Labidosaurus

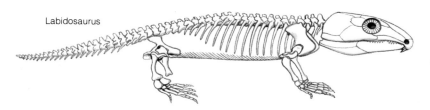

Half amphibian, half reptile

The amphibian anthracosaurs included a group of forms which are significant in mapping out the evolution of the vertebrates: this was the sub-order of Seymouriamorphs. The Seymouriamorphs comprise a certain number of very evolved labyrinthodonts. Among them the best known is the genus *Seymouria* (left), whose skeletons feature characteristics of both reptiles and amphibians. The Seymouriamorphs lived in the Permian Period, when reptiles were already well developed and widely diffused. They are not transitional organisms between these two groups of vertebrates, but rather the direct descendents of transitional organisms not yet identified.

Hylonomus, primitive reptile from the Carboniferous

Intermediary forms

The differences between reptiles and amphibians are not difficult to determine. Both classes have clearly distinguished characteristics at the present time, and this applies both to soft tissues and skeletal structure. It is not so simple, however, to make such clear distinctions based on a number of fossil specimens. One case in point is *Seymouria*, whose mixture of reptilian and amphibian characteristics makes it an intermediary form between the two classes. The diagram below shows how the skull of *Seymouria* has an amphibian type of tympanal cavity **(a)** whereas reptiles **(b)** possess a cavity above the articulation of the jawbones; reptiles have a single occipital condyle **(d)**; amphibians have two **(c)**; vertebrae with a pleurocentre more developed than the intercentre **(e)** as in reptiles **(f)**, and lastly as many phalanxes **(g)** as in a reptile **(h)**.

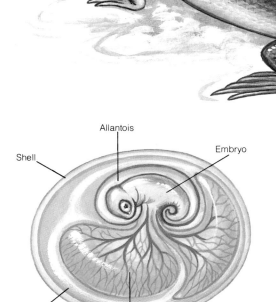

Allantois

Shell

Embryo

Albumen

Yolk

The amniotic egg

The development of the amniotic egg was a major step forward for the vertebrates. In this type of egg, the embryo is surrounded by different membranes (see left); the amnion envelops the embryo, containing it in a watery environment. The allantois has a number of vessels and is used for respiration. There is also a third membrane (chorion) close to the shell.

Semiaquatic reptiles

Although the amniotic egg enabled reptiles to leave behind their aquatic habitat, many of them continued to be tied to it, such as *Limnoscelis* (below), a semiaquatic carnivorous reptile from the Permian.

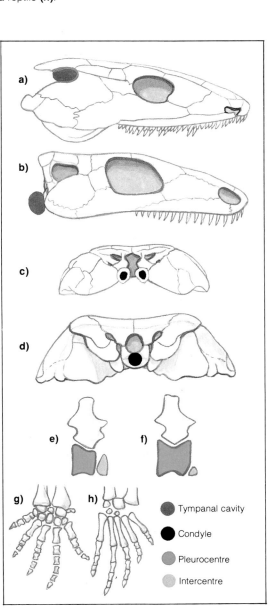

a)

b)

c)

d)

e) f)

g) h)

- ⬤ Tympanal cavity
- ⬤ Condyle
- ⬤ Pleurocentre
- ⬤ Intercentre

Evolution of the reptiles

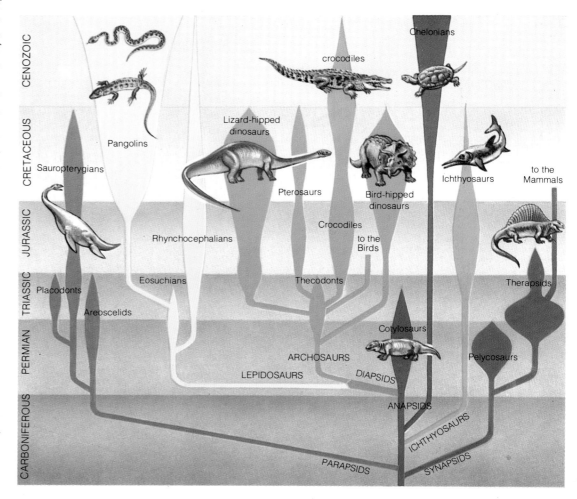

These new vertebrate creatures which could lay an amniotic egg appeared, as we have seen, in the Carboniferous, and developed both quickly and spectacularly. The reptile cotylosaurs, which had evolved from the amphibian labyrinthodonts, developed in a very short time, in keeping with the scale of geological phases, into groups of more evolved reptiles, which lived alongside the primitive cotylosaurs. The evolution of reptiles in the Upper Palaeozoic was so rapid that the term 'explosion' or 'evolutive radiation' is often used to describe the appearance of groups which differed from each other and were increasingly specialised. The reptiles thus began to take over every ecological niche open to the higher vertebrates. Later they dominated the air with pterosaurs, the seas with plesiosaurs and ichthyosaurs, and dry land with dinosaurs. As a result, the Mesozoic era on which they set their stamp is known as the 'age of reptiles'.

Very little is left today of the large groups of reptiles that characterised the Palaeozoic and Mesozoic. The parapsids became extinct in the Cretaceous; the lepidosaurs are represented currently by the pangolins, the lizards and the snakes; of the archosaurs, the great rulers of the dry land with the dinosaurs, only crocodiles are left. The oldest group, the anapsids, is today represented by chelonians, tortoises, and turtles, which are therefore the most primitive reptiles now surviving. The synapsids, eventually, played a leading part in the history of the evolution of vertebrates; from them, through the reptile-mammals, the first real mammals originated.

Classification of reptiles

The classification of the large reptile groups is still the subject of debate among scholars. One type of classification widely used is the one based on the position and number of temporal apertures in the skull. Where no aperture is present, the skull is of the anapsid type (A); a skull with one aperture beneath or above the join between the postorbital bone and the squamosal, is described as the synapsid (B) or parapsid (C) type respectively; a skull with both apertures mentioned is of the diapsid type (D).

The mesosaurs

Of the reptile synapsids, the mesosaurs occupy a prominent place in the Permian Period. Among the best known genera in this group, are *Mesosaurus* (left) and *Stereosternum*. The origin of the mesosaurs is in some respects still obscure: according to some scholars, they have greatest affinity with the reptile group of pelycosaurs, the most primitive synapsids, who appeared in the Upper Carboniferous. The mesosaurs were mostly small, sometimes not much more than a metre in length, and they had a body similar to that of lizards; the jawbones were well developed and bristled with numerous sharp teeth. This provides tangible proof of their ability to feed off fish. Mesosaurs also had a long tail which would have enabled them to swim well. The particular structure of their limbs suggests that they had webbed feet. The overall interest of the mesosaurs lies in their habitat and geographic distribution: on the basis of the characteristics of the rocks in which they have been discovered, they were undoubtedly freshwater reptiles and are found in lakes in South America and South Africa. These reptiles could not have crossed an ocean because they were conditioned to fresh water. This fact was included in the palaeontological evidence put forward by Alfred Wegener, the German geophysicist, to support his theory of continental drift, i.e: that South America and Africa had once been joined, but had become separated in the geological eras.

The Pelycosaurs

During the evolution of the reptiles, a very important group belonging to the primitive synapsids appeared in the Carboniferous. These were the pelycosaurs; they existed at the same time as the progenitor of that large group of reptiles to which the dinosaurs belong — Petrolacosaurus. Petrolacosaurus was an insectivorous animal the size of a lizard, adapted to forest life. At the end of the Carboniferous, the leading group of synapsids enjoyed impressive success and underwent special evolutionary expansion. In the Permian, for instance, there existed *Dimetrodon* which had a large fin-like crest. Dimetrodon, a vegetarian, was three and a half metres long, and possessed a massive frame. The great fin possibly helped Dimetrodon to regulate its body temperature. Because of this structure some palaeontologists believe Dimetrodon took the first step towards being 'warm-blooded'. The first near-mammals appeared much later, at the end of the Permian.

Edaphosaurus

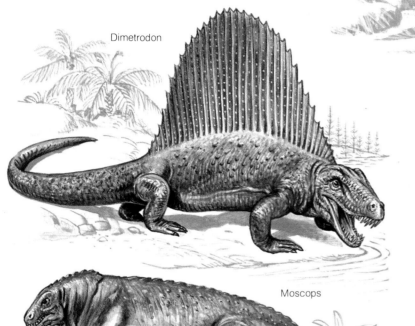

Dimetrodon

Moscops

Reptilian mammals

The two reconstructions here show, on the left, a giant and heavy vegetarian, *Moscops*, from which evolved the dicynodonts including *Lystrosaurus*, right. Lystrosaurus had diversified teeth and two sharp fangs, but nevertheless retained some striking reptilian characteristics.

Lystrosaurus

The synapsids

The first synapsids had an elongated skull with a very large number of teeth to prevent its prey from escaping once caught; it was a kind of grille rather than a proper aid to chewing. Later, the size of their mandibles decreased, enabling them to feed off other small reptiles living on the plains. These mandibles became shorter and stronger, with fewer teeth. The synapsids developed long pointed front teeth to enable them to wound and get a better hold on their prey. The skull also became stronger and inside the mouth a soft palate developed which separated the air-ways from the digestive tracts; this meant the synapsids could breathe easily even while feeding. Left and right: two typical skulls of synapsids, from the South African Permian.

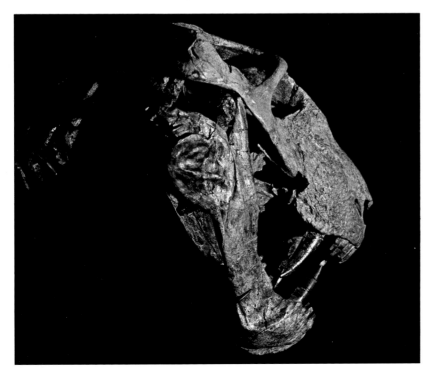

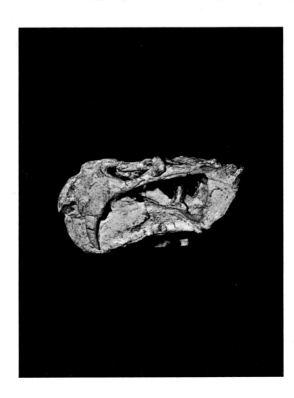

45

The Mesozoic Era

Period	Millions of years ago
CRETACEOUS	140
JURASSIC	195
TRIASSIC	230

The Mesozoic, or Secondary, Era took place between 230 and 65 million years ago. It is subdivided into three periods, which are, first, the Triassic, followed by the Jurassic, and the Cretaceous. In the space of about 165 million years, there was further evolution on a considerable scale both in the geography of our planet and in its fauna and flora. The Mesozoic is also called the 'age of reptiles' because reptiles became so widespread in this era.

The oldest of the three periods, the Triassic, saw life on dry land flourish: the first dinosaurs began to take over the continents, the first mammals made their timid appearance, while flying reptiles took to the air for the first time. In the seas, among the impressive coral barrier reefs, the placodonts, nothosaurs and tortoises found their food by hunting ammonoid cephalopods and belemnites. The Jurassic Period was characterised by a certain climatic stability which favoured the development of marine and terrestrial fauna; the dinosaurs succeeded in populating all the continents which in the Lower Jurassic had still been joined in a single continental land mass called Pangaea; the first bird hovered in the skies, teleost fish, from which modern fish are descended, appeared in the seas, and the cephalopods developed into a number of different forms. The Cretaceous witnessed the disappearance of the dinosaurs, the big marine reptiles, the ammonites, the hippurites and the great coral or barrier reefs. During this period the continents separated. There were climatic variations, and the seas, too, felt the effect of the continental drift which in a few million years completely changed the face of planet Earth.

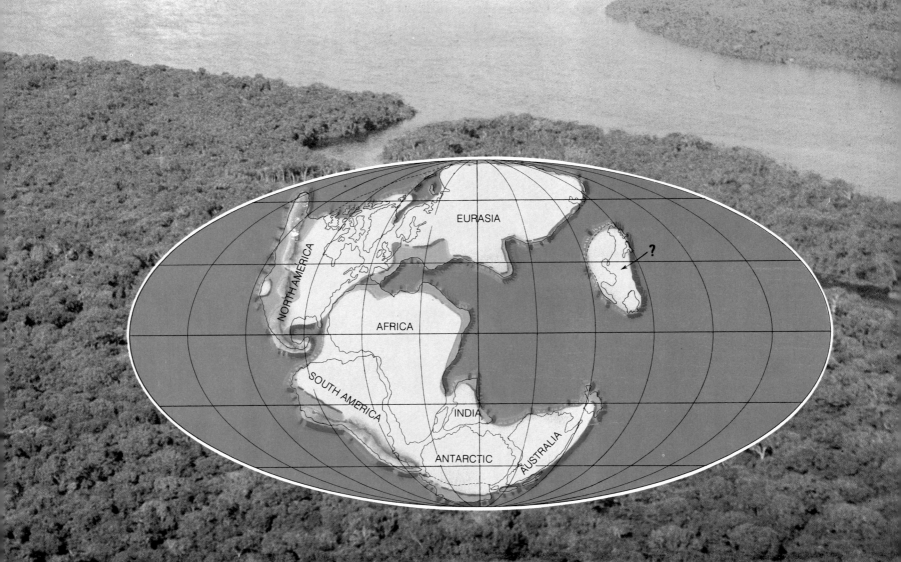

Two typical carnivorous dinosaurs
An Allosaurus (above), a dinosaur belonging to the Saurischian (or lizard-hipped) order, in the typical posture the carnivore adopts when closing on its prey. Standing upright on its strong hind legs, it used its fore legs to grasp the prey before finishing it off with its jaws. *Coelophysis* (below left) was a coelurosaur from the American Triassic. It was a biped dinosaur, a fast runner living in the plains: ceolophysis was discovered during an excavation in 1947 in New Mexico. A very active carnivore, it probably hunted in packs.

The map below shows the main sites where ornithischian or bird-hipped dinosaurs have been found.

Where dinosaurs originated and why they succeeded

Dinosaurs originated from a group of reptiles that were very widespread on the Earth in the Triassic Period — the thecodonts, which literally means 'teeth situated in sockets'. These creatures, together with the Pterosaurs, the crocodiles and the dinosaurs themselves, belong to the sub-class of Archosaurs.

The reptiles classified in this order have a particular pelvic bone structure. In these reptiles the structure of the limbs was modified and able to take on a vertical position under the body. This contrasts with other groups of reptiles which have to crawl rather than walk because the humerus and femur project outwards. The transition to a 'columnar' position made it much easier to walk about. This in turn meant increased speed. The dinosaurs, now less awkward, therefore became more competitive in the struggle for survival. This new structure for walking which first appeared in the thecodonts and later with the dinosaurs, derived from modifications to the scapular girdle and pelvic girdle — in other words, to the 'shoulders' and 'pelvis'. The pelvic girdle became very strong, the sacral vertebrae merged and combined with the pelvic bones, the ilium was expanded and the strong muscles in the legs became fixed to the ischium and the pubis which were themselves transformed from flat to cylindrical.

With the development of hind legs and the adoption of a two-legged stance, the remaining skeletal structures were also transformed: the front part of the body straightened up, the front legs no longer touched the ground, and a long and powerful tail developed as a device for keeping the body balanced during movement.

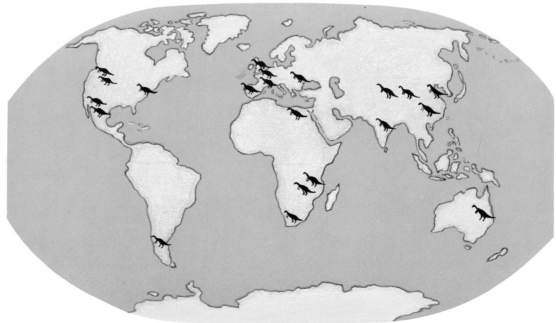

Two major groups of dinosaurs

In the Middle Triassic, two major groups of Dinosaurs appeared: the saurischian, or lizard-hipped dinosaurs and the ornithischian or bird-hipped dinosaurs. These two groups were separated on the initiative of the British palaeontologist Seeley, who in 1888 proposed that they be distinguished from one another on the basis of pelvic bone variation. The order of Saurischians comprises both carnivorous and herbivorous dinosaurs, whereas in the order of Ornithischians only herbivorous dinosaurs are represented. The Saurischians in their turn are divided into two sub-orders: theropods and sauropodomorphs. The theropod sub-order comprises coelurosaurs, carnivorous biped dinosaurs, of small or medium size with thin bones and a lightweight skeleton, and carnosaurs, also carnivorous but on a larger scale, with biped motion and an impressive, very robust skeleton. The sub-order of sauropodomorphs comprises herbivorous dinosaurs, essentially quadrupeds which attained considerable size; to this group the famous Brontosaurus belongs. The Ornithischians are a more heterogeneous group than the Saurischians; exclusively herbivorous, they never attained a biped stance and walked most of the time on all four legs. The Ornithischian group, possessed primitive characteristics such as an armoured skin, as well as advanced features like predentary bone and, in some groups, a horny mouth and a complex set of teeth.

Evolutionary context of the reptiles

Shown here: the reptiles from which the two groups of dinosaurs most probably originated and the forms these most celebrated reptiles adopted in the course of their evolution and life on the Earth.

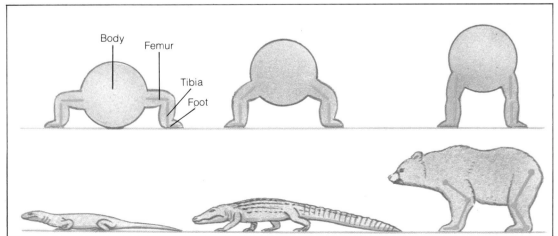

Successive modifications in bearing

The drawing (left) illustrates the typical gaits of a lizard, a crocodile and a mammal, similar to that of the dinosaurs. Note the different positions of the femur and the tibia, which vary from horizontal and vertical respectively to vertical, in other words positioned one above the other.

The dinosaurs

The dinosaurs, having already been in evidence during the Jurassic in a large number of forms, underwent their greatest evolutionary development in the Cretaceous. The typical representatives of the Jurassic are the carnivorous saurischian dinosaurs like Allosaurus, a close relative of Tyrannosaurus, and the small, swift *Compsognathus*, which was barely larger than a chicken. The herbivorous dinosaurs are represented by Diplodocus and Brontosaurus, both giant reptiles over twenty metres long. The ornithischians were represented by *Camptosaurus*, a herbivorous semibiped that was easy prey for Allosaurus, and by the stegosaurs with their heavy protective armour-plating on the back and tail.

In the Cretaceous Period these animals were superseded by later generations, some of them far evolved. Among them were the carnivorous dinosaurs including the powerful-jawed Tyrannosaurus. Another carnivorous dinosaur was *Deinonychus*, the most agile of hunters, whose powerful claws did not touch the ground as it walked, suggesting that it was well adapted to jumping. Ornithischian dinosaurs with strange carapaces also appeared: the ankylosaurs, *Iguanodon*, and the pachycephalosaurs. These dinosaurs, whose heads were shielded by a solid bony plate, took the place of *Camptosaurus*, their immediate antecedent.

The Hadrosaurs were undoubtedly the most diffused dinosaur group in the Cretaceous. Also called duck-billed dinosaurs, these herbivorous relatives of *Camptosaurus* had heads flattened over a beak-shaped mouth. The Hadrosaurs had a talent for adaptation. Through a series of variations to the head and the masticatory apparatus they came to be diffused over the whole Earth and enjoyed considerable success.

The ceratopians

The Cretaceous marked the appearance of dinosaurs with big bony collars, the ceratopians. These tripled their size in a few million years and from their origins in Mongolia came to inhabit the entire Earth.

The illustration above features the famous Triceratops, which lived in the savannahs of North America. This giant herbivore was more than eight metres long and three metres high. It had a well developed skull with three sturdy horns which it used to defend itself and strip plants of their leaves. Triceratops also possessed a beak which could dig out and pull up the roots it fed on. In the back part of the skull, there was a bony structure in the form of a collar, with pointed plates along it. Beside protecting a particularly vulnerable part of its body, this provided a broad anchoring surface for the muscles which supported the heavy head.

Reconstruction and skeleton of Diplodocus, a giant herbivorous saurischian dinosaur.

Scheme of evolution of the dinosaurs

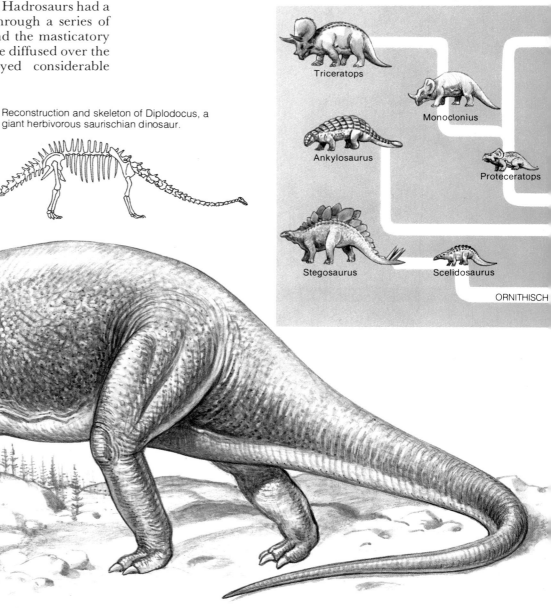

Triceratops

Monoclonius

Ankylosaurus

Proteceratops

Stegosaurus

Scelidosaurus

ORNITHISCH

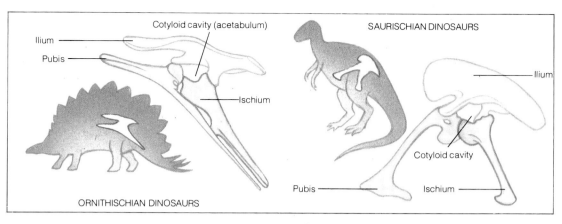

Cotyloid cavity (acetabulum)

Ilium

Pubis

Ischium

ORNITHISCHIAN DINOSAURS

SAURISCHIAN DINOSAURS

Ilium

Cotyloid cavity

Pubis

Ischium

Dinosaur deposits

Dinosaurs lived in regions with a mild climate, near big stretches of fresh water. Their skeletons have therefore been found on the beds of lakes. The most famous dinosaur deposits are in North America where excavations are still being carried out. In Europe and in Asia, remains of dinosaurs have been found. Most notable is a deposit in Belgium where the skeletons of a group of *Iguanodon*, killed by falling into a ravine, were discovered between strata of coal; nests with dinosaur eggs have been found in Mongolia. In Africa, in a narrow strip of territory 150 kilometres long, fossil plants, reptiles and dinosaurs have come to light, in what remains of a great prehistoric lake.

Anatomy of the dinosaurs

In the above diagram the different positions of the pelvic bones in ornithischian and saurischian dinosaurs can be seen. In the upper region of the femur in dinosaurs, known as the head of the femur, a joint developed which came to be hinged in the cotyloid cavity, the niche formed by the three pelvic bones. The presence of a joint between femur and cotyloid cavity meant that the leg could be moved forwards and backwards.

Reconstruction of Tyrannosaurus, the fiercest of the carnivorous dinosaurs.

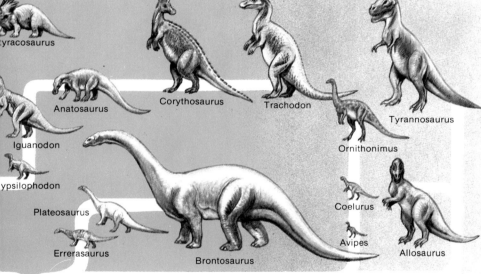

Styracosaurus

Anatosaurus

Corythosaurus

Trachodon

Tyrannosaurus

Iguanodon

Ornithonimus

ypsilophodon

Plateosaurus

Coelurus

Errerasaurus

Avipes

Brontosaurus

Allosaurus

SAURISCHIANS

THECODONTS

Tyrannosaurus

Tyrannosaurus was the most terrible and gigantic of carnivores ever seen on Earth. About 15 metres long and six metres high, it weighed over ten tons. Tyrannosaurus inhabited the plateaux and lowlands of the Cretaceous and successfully hunted 'duck-billed' dinosaurs, the giant sauropodomorphs and ceratopians. According to some palaeontologists, Tyrannosaurus moved slowly and heavily, with short strides. Its chief weapons were the three strong claws on its hind legs which it used to tear open its prey after catching and felling it; its terrible jaws had sharp teeth more adept at tearing the meat than clutching at its prey, as was thought until quite recently. The forelegs, reduced to stumps, were of very little use except for support when Tyrannosaurus had to get up off the ground.

The first flying reptiles

The Upper Triassic in Lombardy has produced remains of the oldest known flying reptiles, *Eudimorphodon* (left) and *Peteinosaurus*. The two flying reptiles, while still having primitive features, were already well evolved and diversified. To judge from its teeth *Eudimorphodon* fed on small fish, whereas *Peteinosaurus* probably preferred to feed on insects.

Adapting to flight

Terrestrial vertebrates had tried several times to master flight and their bone structure became modified to cope with the different requirements involved in the aerial rather than the terrestrial setting. Reptiles became adapted to flying by means of a cutaneous wing membrane stretched between the body and the well-developed fourth digit on its front legs. With birds, of course, the wing surface is made up of a series of feathers, whereas with flying mammals — bats — the membrane is supported by the 2nd, 3rd, 4th and 5th fingers, all of them very elongated. Left: An outline of the skull of a rhamphorhynchoid flying reptile, *Dimorphodon*.

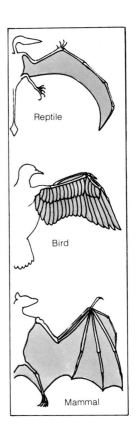

Reptile

Bird

Mammal

Birds and flying reptiles

One of the most fascinating chapters in the history of the evolution of the vertebrates began in the Triassic Period: at that time, they made their first attempt at flying. Until then, only insects had been able to suspend themselves freely in the atmosphere. It fell to the reptile archosaurs, which included dinosaurs and crocodiles, to take on the challenge. The earliest forms of flying reptile are now classified in a proper order Pterosauria, which in ancient Greek meant 'winged reptiles'. Pterosauria possessed characteristics which till then had made them largely unfitted to life in the air. Their heavy skulls had large mouths bristling with teeth, and they had elongated tails. However, in the course of evolution they exchanged these features for a horny beak and aeriferous bones. Some Pterosauria achieved very considerable size: *Quetzalcoatlus*, a reptile of the North American Cretaceous, had a wing-span of about 14 metres; it was the largest living creature ever to take to the air. Flying reptiles developed a remarkably large brain. Some furred specimens suggest a cooling system similar to that of mammals, and very much more efficient than that of reptiles. However, another animal group which also originated from the reptiles managed even greater success in flying. In 1861, in a limestone cave dating from the Upper Jurassic in Bavaria, a fossil came to light which was to become famous throughout the world: this was the half-reptile half-bird known as *Archaeopteryx*. Archaeopteryx is the oldest bird yet discovered and was one of the few to live in the Mesozoic. At that time the skies were still dominated by the flying reptiles and it was only after they became totally extinct, at the end of the Cretaceous, that birds could achieve full development.

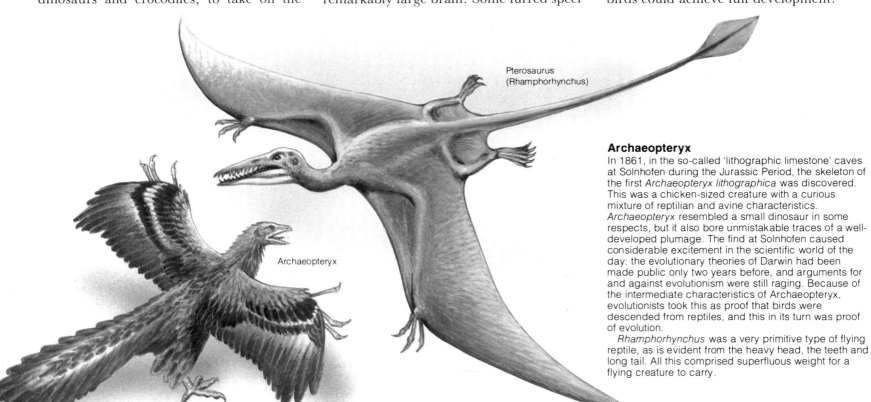

Pterosaurus (Rhamphorhynchus)

Archaeopteryx

Archaeopteryx

In 1861, in the so-called 'lithographic limestone' caves at Solnhofen during the Jurassic Period, the skeleton of the first *Archaeopteryx lithographica* was discovered. This was a chicken-sized creature with a curious mixture of reptilian and avine characteristics. *Archaeopteryx* resembled a small dinosaur in some respects, but it also bore unmistakable traces of a well-developed plumage. The find at Solnhofen caused considerable excitement in the scientific world of the day: the evolutionary theories of Darwin had been made public only two years before, and arguments for and against evolutionism were still raging. Because of the intermediate characteristics of Archaeopteryx, evolutionists took this as proof that birds were descended from reptiles, and this in its turn was proof of evolution.

Rhamphorhynchus was a very primitive type of flying reptile, as is evident from the heavy head, the teeth and long tail. All this comprised superfluous weight for a flying creature to carry.

Reptiles in flight

A reconstruction of the flight of a *Rhamphorhynchus* (right) which, after taking off from the top of a rock, has managed to catch a fish. Most flying reptiles lived on the reefs that rose out of the seas in the Mesozoic. From these, they dived, then glided long distances in search of prey. They must have spent most of their time in the air, using to advantage the movement of the air-currents to remain stabilised; on the ground, though, they moved with great difficulty, in view of the major disproportion between their fore- and hind-legs. Right: *Pterodactylus*, a flying reptile from the Upper Jurassic in Germany.

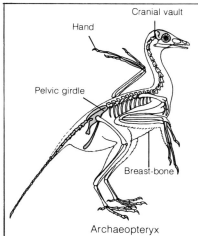

Evolution of the skeleton

A comparison between the skeletons of *Archaeopteryx* (left) and a modern pigeon (right). Although it possessed plumage, a characteristic exclusive to birds, *Archaeopteryx* differs substantially in a number of skeletal details. It has an elongated tail, whereas birds have a shortened caudal skeleton ending in the pygostyle, the bone that supports the rectrices in the tail. With *Archaeopteryx*, the foreleg has three free digits with talons, the mouth contains teeth and it does not have a carinate breast-bone; also, the bones, unlike those of birds, are not hollow.

Archaeopteryx

Modern pigeon

Hesperornis

Ichthyornis

Pteranodon

In the skies of the Upper Cretaceous

In the lagoons of the Upper Cretaceous in North America there lived two genera of birds of a much more modern type than *Archaeopteryx*, even though they retained a mouthful of teeth. *Hesperornis* (on the left in the drawing), about one metre in height was not well suited to flying. It was probably a diver more tied to the sea than the air, as modern penguins are. *Ichthyornis* (in the middle) had strong teeth, was good at flying and must have led a life-style similar to that of modern sea-gulls. The skies of the Upper Cretaceous were streaked most of all by the best evolved of the flying reptiles, such as *Pteranodon* (above right). This reptile, which achieved a wing-span of more than seven metres, had developed a toothless horny beak and hollow bones. It had no tail. Pteranodon could glide long distances over the seas with the aid of air-currents.

53

Marine reptiles

While dinosaurs were establishing themselves on the dry land and pterosaurs were dominating the skies, other reptiles were becoming rulers of the seas. Since the amphibians began to populate dry land, in the Palaeozoic, no four-legged animal (tetrapod) had managed to return to the sea: marine amphibians were rare and not especially widespread. However, from the Triassic Period onwards, numerous groups of reptiles attempted to secure the huge ecological niche represented by the shallow seas that partly covered the continental shields. Some of them achieved temporary success while others developed throughout the Mesozoic and gave rise to increasingly specialised forms adapted to marine life. The placodonts, reptiles somewhat resembling modern tortoises, lived exclusively in the Triassic; the nothosaurs were particularly widespread: their remains have been found in very large quantities in the famous deposit of Besano-Monte San Giorgio.

Different genera have come to light, including *Pachypleurosaurus* and *Ceresiosaurus*. The nothosaurs have a slender shape and flattened limbs, elongated neck and small skull, all of which indicates an adaptation to marine life which would later be perfected in the plesiosaurs. Crocodiles also had marine forms during the Jurassic Period: the geosaurs, for instance, had flippers on their limbs and a tail that could be used for propulsion.

The giant mosasaurs, big marine lizards as long as ten metres, appeared in the Cretaceous. However, two other groups claimed the greatest diffusion: the dolphin-shaped ichthyosaurs and the plesiosaurs. The fate of the marine reptiles must, however, have been very much the same as that of the dinosaurs and pterosaurs: they became almost completely extinct near to the transition from the Mesozoic Era to the Cenozoic.

The plesiosaurs
During the Jurassic and the Cretaceous, the giant plesiosaurs (above) were present in all the seas on Earth. Some plesiosaurs were as long as 13 metjres; their limbs had been transformed into flippers and their bodies were flattened. Like the ichthyosaurs, these reptiles may never have left the water, where their diet consisted of fish caught with quick movements of their long and flexible necks.

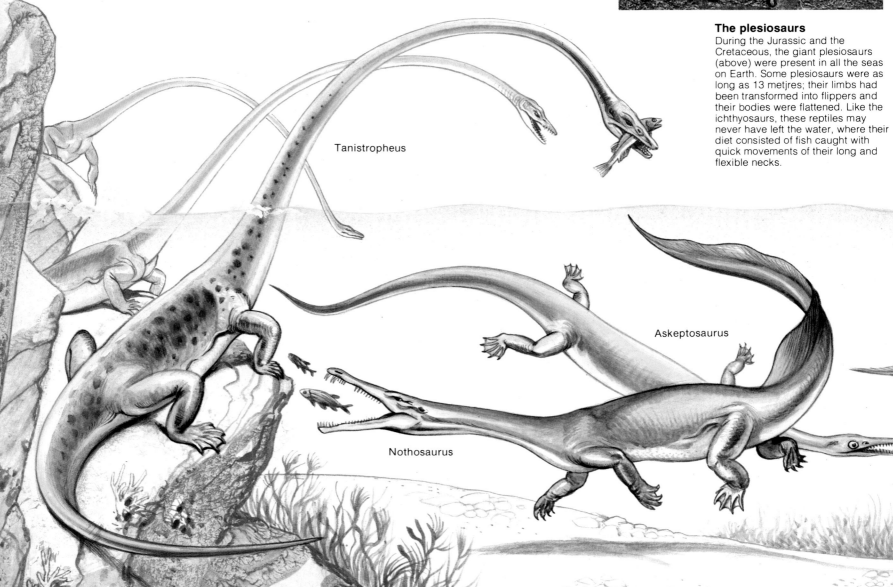

Tanistropheus

Askeptosaurus

Nothosaurus

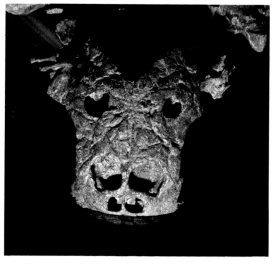

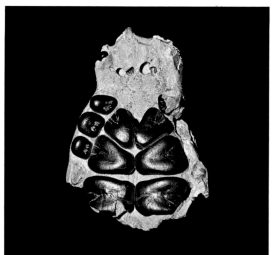

The placodonts

The placodonts are marine reptiles exclusive to the European Triassic. Sometimes they had a carapace similar to that of the modern tortoise, although the two creatures are in no way related. The limbs of placodonts were not highly specialised to cope with aquatic life. This suggests that placodonts resorted to dry land for at least part of their life, for instance to lay their eggs. The teeth which gave them their name are possibly their most curious characteristic, differentiating them from the other reptiles. Placodonts possess numerous teeth in a plate which completely cover their mandibles and jaws. Teeth of this type must have been useful to help placodonts feed on animals like lamellibranchs and brachipods, which were very plentiful in the seas at that time. The placodonts would grind down the shell after tearing the creature up from the sea bed. Above left, and left: a skull of *Henodus* with characteristic teeth.

The ichthyosaurs

The ichthyosaurs represent a group that was widely dispersed throughout the Mesozoic Era. This group was completely adapted to marine life. This is evident from their perfectly streamlined shape, similar to that of a fish. this shape would later feature in other tetrapods which had returned to the sea — the cetacean mammals. The fish outline of the ichthyosaurs complete with dorsal fin and bilobate tail, has been determined by a number of exceptionally well preserved fossils in which all details are intact (above). The ichthyosaurs, whose name means reptile-fish, were so well adapted to life at sea that they produced live young, rather than laying eggs like the land reptiles. They had good carnivore teeth and probably fed on fish, especially on mollusc cephalopods, which were very plentiful in the seas of that time.

In the seas of the Mesozoic

The reconstruction below brings together marine reptiles which lived at different times in the Mesozoic Era. *Tanystropheus* (far left), is one of the most curious, with its long neck which must have been used for pulling in the fish it fed on. *Askeptosaurus* was a semiaquatic reptile and a fearsome predator, while in the centre of the picture there are two placodonts: the armour-plated *Henodus* and *Psephoderma*, seen tugging bivalves from the sea bed. Note the flippers on *Plesiosaurus*, similar to a turtle's. By contrast, the limbs of the more primitive *Nothosaurus* are less specialised.

Nothosaurus

Plesiosaurus

Henodus

Psephoderma

Lystrosaurus

Cynognatus

Bauria

Morganucodon

Thrinaxodon

Triconodon

Evolution of the mandible

The diagram below shows how the mandible evolved from the age of synapsids to the age of mammals. With the pelycosaurs (1), the dental bone is thin and little developed, and the teeth are not particularly diversified; with the therapsids (2, 3), the dental bone is more developed, the incisors and canines diversified first, followed by canine teeth at the back of the mouth which tended to act as molars. With the mammals (4), the numerous bones supporting the dental bone disappeared, and the dental bone itself became stronger and contained diversified teeth.

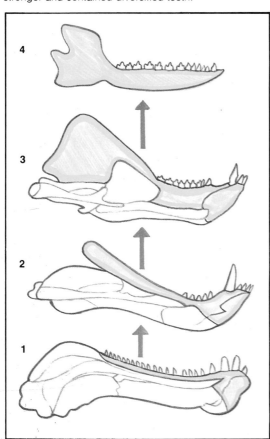

Origin of the mammals

In the Upper Palaeozoic, there lived a group of reptiles known as synapsids whose morphological characteristics are especially notable.

Synapsid characteristics are typical of both reptiles and mammals, which accounts for their classification as 'reptile-mammals'. They appeared in the Carboniferous and became widely dispersed during the Permian before they eventually became extinct in the Jurassic. Synapsids are subdivided into two major orders, the pelycosaurs and the therapsids. The older of the two, the pelycosaurs, produced *Dimetrodon*, a very strange creature with a large 'sail' on its back. The therapsid group produced *Cynognathus*, *Thrinaxodon*, *Bauria* and *Lystrosaurus*.

The transition from 'reptile-mammals' to 'mammals' is not marked by a quantum jump in evolution. It occurred gradually, with these reptiles slowly acquiring mammal characteristics. In the Upper Triassic the first true mammal appeared in Europe. This was the insectivorous *Morganucodon*, a singular creature not much bigger than a shrew. Morganucodon was followed, in the Jurassic, by *Triconodon*, a carnivore which fed on small reptiles and probably had a body covered in thick fur.

Characteristics of mammals

Mammals differ from reptiles in a number of bodily structures: the former featured a body covered in hairs, mammary glands, ears consisting of three small bones, and a joint between the mandible and the skull.

In reptiles the mandible joints hinged on two bones, one in the skull and the other as part of the mandible. In mammals, by contrast, the mandible comprises a single bone which has a direct joint with the skull. The two bones forming that joint in reptiles (the quadrate bone or rectangular and the articular or jointed bone) are situated in the area of the middle ear where they transmit sound vibrations from the tympanum to the inner ear.

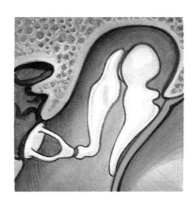

Evolution of mammals

The chart on this page details the three main lines along which modern mammals evolved: in blue, the marsupials, in brown, the placental mammals, and in yellow, the monotremes. It is evident that a big evolutionary explosion occurred in the Cretaceous, resulting in the disappearance of the dinosaurs. The marsupials, which came on to the scene in the Cretaceous, probably derived from a mammal group which already existed in the Jurassic. These were the pantotheres, which in the course of their history do not evince great evolutionary variations. The placentals diversified from the pantotheres in the Cretaceous. Within this group, there is a distinction between proteutheres, from which the carnivores developed along with the primates and numerous other groups, and the condylarths, which were the origin of all herbivorous creatures living in the world today. Not all the groups which derived from these two initial stocks have survived to the present time: for example, extinction claimed the creodonts and teniodonts, which derived from the proteutheres, a large number of groups deriving from the condylarths. The origin of the monotremes is uncertain; some scientists believe they derived from the triconodonts, others that monotremes should not be regarded as mammals at all, because of their many reptilian attributes.

So, just as the dinosaurs were dominant in the Mesozoic Era, the mammals assumed this leading role in the Cenozoic Era. They still retain it today after 64 million years of unopposed supremacy.

The Dicynodonts

The skull in the photo below is of *Dicynodon*, a reptile-mammal of the Therapsid group discovered in Upper Permian layers at Karroo in South Africa. Dicynodonts became extinct in the Upper Triassic.

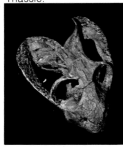

Marsupials

Marsupials are mammals with a pouch or marsupium. The female gives birth to live, though not completely developed, young. The young animal is helped by its mother to get into the pouch where it is attached permanently to a nipple. When the young leaves the pouch, it continues to be suckled by the mother until weaning, but with a different type of milk.

Placentals

These are without doubt the most evolved of the mammals. The embryo grows in the mother's womb and is well protected by her body; nourishment passes into the placenta through a system of blood vessels which also serve to drain off the waste matter produced by the embryo. Some of the young can walk as soon as they are born; others need to be cared for by the mother over a longer period.

Monotremes

Monotremes possess the oldest-established mammalian characteristics. Monotreme embryos develop inside an egg within the mother's uterus and after-birth are carried in a pouch (like echidnas) or laid in a nest. Suckling is primitive: the young feed by licking the milk produced by a double series of glands that runs down the fur on the mother's belly.

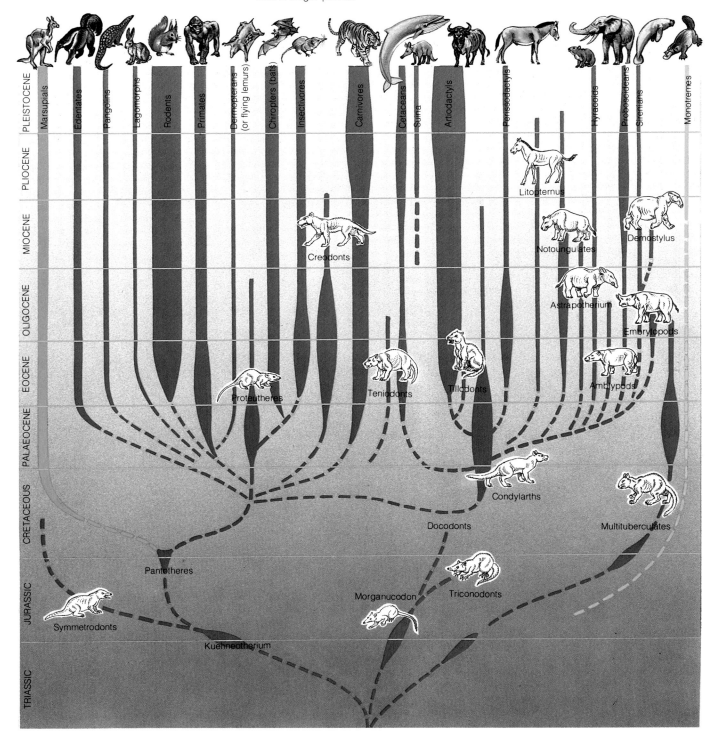

Ammonites

The ammonoids, commonly known as ammonites, are among the best known and most numerous marine fossils of the Mesozoic Era. They belong to the cephalopod molluscs which had a variously ornamented exterior shell, usually coiled into the shape of a flat spiral. This, like that of the modern *Nautilus* was subdivided into a succession of chambers separated by 'septa'. The line of the insertion of the septa on the shell, usually visible in fossil remains, is called the suture line, and came to form a very complex pattern on ammonites from the Jurassic and Cretaceous. The suture line is one of the features used in the zoological classification of these animals. The ammonites enjoyed peak dispersion from the Triassic onwards. They were so abundant in rocks, so widespread in area and evolved so rapidly that they are of primary importance for the stratigraphical subdivision of marine sediments of the Mesozoic Era.

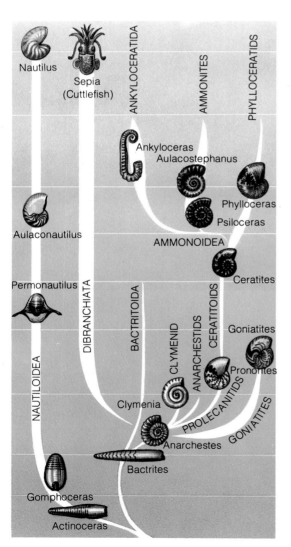

Evolution of the ammonites

The chart shows the evolutionary paths of the major groups of ammonites. In all probability, the most primitive forms of ammonites derive from a group very close to the *Bactritoida* — nautiloids which had a developed shell, that is, not coiled in a spiral. From this group, in the Palaeozoic, come the *Goniatites* and the *Clymenids*, with a very simple suture line and scanty or no ornamentation. At the start of the Mesozoic Era, in the Triassic Period, the *Ceratitoids* underwent major development. This was distinguished by a suture line, though still with little complex ornamentation, which gave rise to the three big groups: *Lytoceras Cornucopia*, *Ammonites* and *Phylloceratida*. These three developed greatly in the Jurassic and Cretaceous. These groups feature the richest and most diverse forms when it comes to ornamentation and the complexity of the suture line, however, survived the biological crisis which marked the end of the Mesozoic Era.

Ammonites

An ammonite of the genus *Amaltheus* (above), which lived at the start of the Jurassic Period, a period which saw the ammonites attain the peak of their dispersion. It features a shell coiled in the distinctive flat spiral and an elegant ornamentation of regularly spaced ribbing.

Ammonite structures

The shell is not the only part of ammonites to be preserved: in Mesozoic soils, there are a large number of single or coupled remains of calcareous structures, which were once regarded as the remains of crustaceans or as lids designed to close up the shell.

It would seem, however, that these developed parts of the masticatory apparatus and only later on did they assume the function of opercula.

The drawing (right) shows what the masticatory apparatus of the ammonites must have been like. It resembles that of present-day cephalopods like the cuttlefish (sepia) and the polyp.

Morphology of the ammonites

The present-day cephalopod molluscs usually have an internal shell (as in the common 'cuttlebone', for instance), whereas only the Nautilus possesses an external shell. It features marked similarities to the ammonites' shell, both from a morphological and a functional point of view. The shell of the Nautilus, like that of the ammonites, serves as an organ of ballast: the chambers of the shell fill with and empty liquid through the siphon. This varies the specific weight of the animal and enables it to dive or rise in the water. Below left: an outline of the shell of an ammonite. Below right: through-section of a present-day Nautilus.

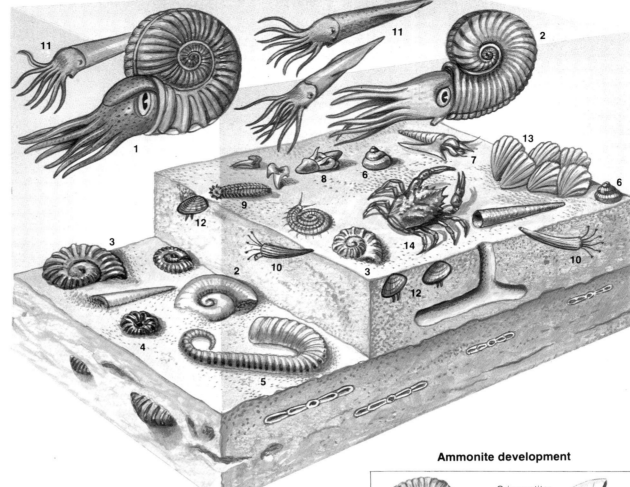

Ammonites:	**1** Mortoniceras
	2 Anahoplites
	3 Hystoceras
	4 Dimorphoplites
	5 Hamites
Gasteropods:	**6** Pleurotomaria
	7 Anchura
	8 Gyrodes
Crinozoans:	**9** Nielsenicrinus
Scaphopods:	**10** Dentalium
Cephalopods:	**11** Neohibolites
Bivalves:	**12** Nucula
	13 Actinoceramus
Crustaceans:	**14** Notopocorystes

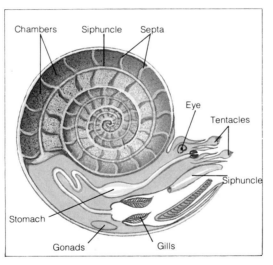

Shell · Peristome · Chambers · Septa

Chambers · Siphuncle · Septa · Eye · Tentacles · Siphuncle · Stomach · Gonads · Gills

Ammonite development

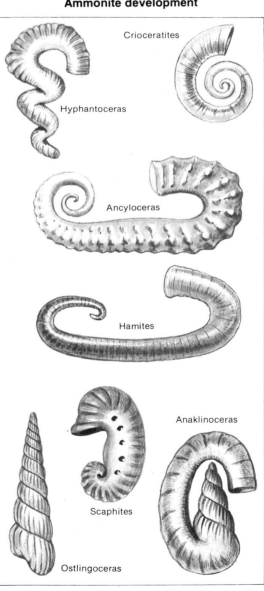

Crioceratites · Hyphantoceras · Ancyloceras · Hamites · Scaphites · Anaklinoceras · Ostlingoceras

Forms of ammonite

During the Mesozoic, ammonites grew especially large, as in the case of a specimen of Parapuzosia (left). As well as the flat-spiral cciled shell, forms evolved with trochoid shells, similar to the familiar gasteropod type (above left), or developed forms, as in the genus Hamites (above right).

Extinction

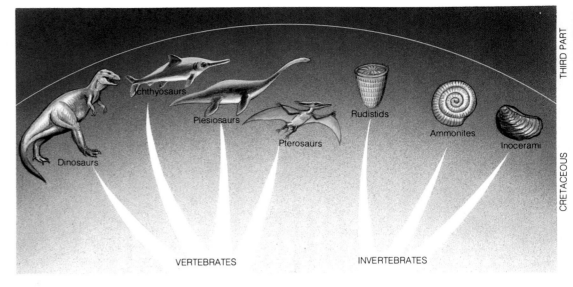

VERTEBRATES   INVERTEBRATES

One of the problems which continues to fascinate palaeontologists is the disappearance of a number of groups of animals, a phenomenon which occurred suddenly and repeatedly in the course of Earth's history. Extinction was especially conspicuous on two occasions: at the end of the Permian and at the end of the Cretaceous. In the Palaeozoic crisis, marine organisms were most involved, in particular the trilobites and the graptolites, while in the crisis of the Upper Cretaceous the ammonites and the best-known dinosaurs disappeared.

Extinctions at the end of the Cretaceous
The extinction of an animal group has great importance. In the last twenty years, many theories have attempted to explain it. Some theories have proved acceptable and debatable; others can only be classed as fantasy explanations. The chart shows the principal groups to become extinct at the end of the Cretaceous 65 million years ago.

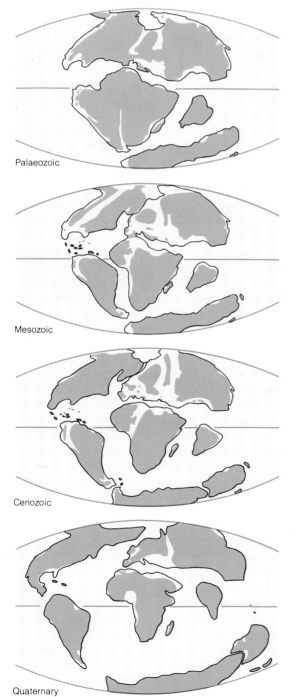

Palaeozoic

Mesozoic

Cenozoic

Quaternary

The drifting continents
The maps (left) show how the geography of our planet substantially altered in the course of the different Eras: the continents became separated and joined again several times before reaching the position they now occupy. This phenomenon is connected with the theory of plate tectonics. In the Upper Palaeozoic, and more precisely at the end of the Permian, the continents joined to form a single continental land mass named Pangaea. Pangaea was split climatically into two super-continents, Laurasia to the North, and Gondwanaland to the South. The rejoining of the continental blocs coincided with the disappearance of a number of groups of marine invertebrates, among them the trilobites and the graptolites. In the Mesozoic, during the Jurassic Period, the continents began to drift apart and new oceans formed, including the Atlantic Ocean. Fossils provide proof of these drift movements, as does a group of dinosaurs found in different continents. It seemed impossible that these animals could have crossed the oceans to inhabit islands like Australia. The mystery was solved by establishing that during the age of the dinosaurs, the continental land masses had been joined. This group of reptiles was therefore able to populate once contiguous areas of the Earth which are now geographically far apart.

Disappearance of the ammonites
The abundance of their remains ensured that the ammonites are today one of the best-known of fossil groups. Until a few years ago they were thought to have lived in all Earth's seas. However, when it was discovered that not all the forms were present in the same sea it became clear that the life of the ammonites was linked to physical factors of temperature and water salinity. This animal group failed to adapt and so disappeared when the movement of the continents, in the Cretaceous, caused environmental and climatic variations.

Distribution of the iguanodons at the end of the Cretaceous

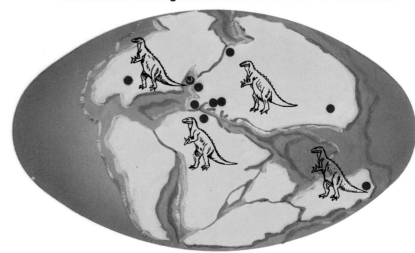

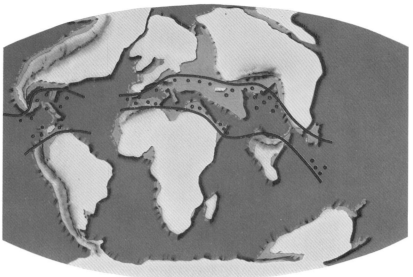

Coral reefs

As can be seen from the map (left) there were a large number of coral reefs to be found in the Cretaceous in a long narrow sea called Tethys. The reefs were not only populated by coral builders. Also present were other animal groups with strange forms which have not survived. These included bivalves shaped like cornucopia (below left), or double horns (below right). In the cornucaprians the shell is coiled in the shape of a horn, in the hippurites, it grows like a coral; in both cases, one of the valves is reduced to form an operculum. These forms are called convergence forms, as these lamellibranchs adapted their shell to the reef in whose clefts they were living. When the super-continent Pangaea split up, Tethys was caught up in the motions of continental drift. As the great land mass bordered by Tethys moved, the sea was transformed first into a series of small marine basins, and afterwards, it disappeared. This was also the end of the remarkable coral reefs and of the strange animals which lived on them.

Coral reefs

Cornucaprians

Hippurites

The theories

Scientists have put forward numerous theories to explain the extinction of the dinosaurs and the ammonites, and the disappearance of the large fossil reefs which existed in the Mesozoic. Some postulate that these groups disappeared because of a stellar explosion and the consequent radiation which would then have bombarded the Earth. This does not, however, explain the survival of some groups while others closely related became extinct. Another theory has it that the ammonites and the dinosaurs, having reached the end of their evolution in the Upper Cretaceous, simply aged and died out. More likely, though, is the idea that extinctions in the Upper Cretaceous were due to a chain-reaction of factors: the separating of the super-continent Pangaea into new island-continents, the climatic and environmental variations resulting from this tectonic movement, and the variations in sea-level which rose appreciably in the Cretaceous only to recede later on to very low levels. In the course of these enormous changes, animal groups with a closer relation to the territory they occupied were unable to adapt and so died out.

The Dinosaurs

The dinosaurs inhabited a large part of the Earth's land surface. They were most prolific in areas with a constant temperature, like the basins of lakes, and particularly calm climatic belts such as the present-day tropics. The movement of the continental land-masses not only resulted in climate change with variations in rainfall and temperature, but the places where the shores were populated by these animals were partially covered by the sea. Thus animals too closely tied to their habitat could not move away in search of a more hospitable setting. Such a move would not, of course, have been of the slightest use, since the continents were no longer connected. So these unfortunate creatures became extinct. Right: palaeontologists at work on salvaging fossil bones of dinosaurs in the Dinosaur National Park (Utah)

The Cenozoic, also termed the Tertiary or Recent Era, occupied Earth's history from between 65 and two million years ago. It is subdivided into five periods which are, first, the Palaeocene, then the Eocene, the Oligocene, the Miocene and the Pliocene.

The Cenozoic is also known as the 'age of the mammals' owing to their widespread presence at this time. With the disappearance of the dinosaurs the mammals found many ecological niches open to them which had previously been occupied by these fascinating reptiles. Subsequently, the mammals quickly spread over every continent. In both herbivorous and carnivorous forms, mammals occupied first the undergrowth and the forests, then ventured onto the great plains, exchanging their small-scale frame for larger, sometimes giant forms. They also attempted to inhabit the skies in the form of bats, and the seas as whales and dolphins, coming to occupy the ecological niche once owned by the ichthyosaurs during the Mesozoic. On dry land, flowering plants colonised forests and grasslands.

The Cenozoic was characterised by a certain climatic stability which favoured the evolutionary expansion of fauna and flora. The geographical appearance of the planet underwent substantial alteration before the end of the Era, when it took on much of its present day appearance. At the same time impressive mountain ranges, including the Alps, were being formed.

The Cenozoic Era

Period	Millions of years ago
PLIOCENE	5
MIOCENE	22
OLIGOCENE	40
EOCENE	55
PALAEOCENE	65

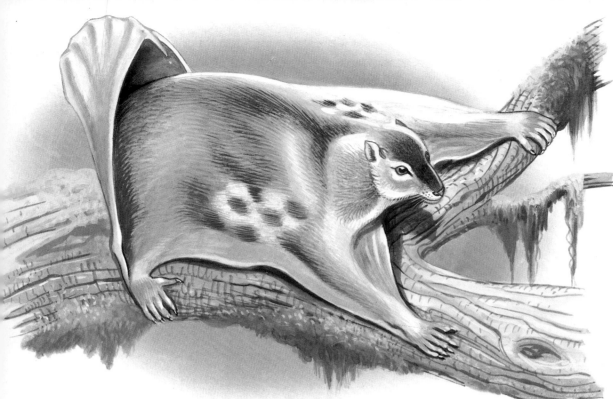

The most spectacular of the earliest placental mammals, which had adapted to life in the trees and were structured for gliding downwards, are those belonging to the group of flying lemurs (or dermopterans). These included *Planetotherium* (left), which inhabited North America and Europe in the Palaeocene. Together with this strange animal there lived squirrels, marmots and the first lagomorphs, the antecedents of modern rabbits. The forests were therefore densely populated by small mammals, and a group of these, the condylarth mammals, lived in the undergrowth and on the earliest lowlands. From the condylarths there later descended the perissodactyls and the artiodactyls, both typical herbivorous mammals.

The evolution of mammals

Mammals, the descendants of reptile synapsids, already inhabited dry land when dinosaurs were the dominant species. The first mammals, the size of shrews, were nocturnal in their habits. When the dinosaurs died out, they quickly occupied the now vacant ecological niches. However, for several million years more they led a specifically tree-dwelling and underwood life. Already in the initial phase in their evolution, two groups of mammals were apparent by their differing feeding habits: the carnivores and the herbivores. Both herbivorous and carnivorous mammals had two enemies in common: one, on dry land, was the gigantic flightless *Diatryma* bird. The other was the crocodiles in the rivers and lakes.

In the course of their evolution the mammals diversified into three main groups: first, the monotremes, now found only in Australia and New Guinea, which represent the most primitive of the groups and number the curious duckbilled platypus among them; second, the marsupials, found in the Americas and in Australasia, and third, the placental mammals, which include human beings.

The Edentates

The Edentates comprise one of the most interesting groups to populate South America. Edentates were so called because of the very simple form, or sometimes complete absence, of teeth. The Glyptodonts, similar to armadilloes, belong to this group. They had a robust carapace and a tail spiked like the mace of a mediaeval knight. These features also occurred in armadilloes and bradypodids, land-dwelling giants (like *Megatherium*, right), which had powerful claws for digging or reaching leaves on very tall trees and shrubs.

Teeth

Mammals and reptiles differ in several bodily structures: fur, a complex ear, method of reproduction, and most of all teeth. Reptile teeth are simple, not greatly varied and used principally to get hold of their prey. Mammals, on the other hand, also use their teeth to chew. Below left: the teeth of the mammal *Demostyllus*. Right: typical teeth of an omnivore, a mountain lion living in the Quaternary.

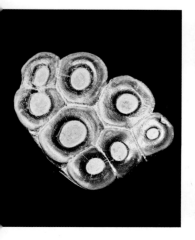

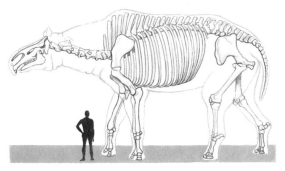

The great herbivores

Two parallel groups of herbivores became distinct during the evolution of the mammals: perissodactyls and artiodactyls. Both derived from a common progenitor, but adopted a different manner of walking and running. The number of toes on various perissodactyls, whether on the front or back leg, is never the same: for example, the horse has one and the rhinoceros has three. By contrast, in artiodactyls, like cervids and hippopotamuses, the number of toes is equal. The animals in these two groups are heavyweights, but are all fast on their feet and agile. Certain perissodactyls grew to a truly remarkable size, such as *Baluchitherium* (above) which reached eight metres in length and a height of five metres at the shoulder-blades.

Monotreme mammals

The duck-billed platypus (above) belongs to a very primitive group of mammals, the monotremes. These creatures reproduce by laying eggs and in many ways resemble reptiles. Once born, the platypus feeds by licking the milk produced by a double row of glands on the belly of the mother which, in contrast with more evolved mammals, does not possess nipples.

Oreodonts

The skull shown below belongs to an *Oreodon*, an artiodactyl very widespread in North America during the Oligocene. *Oreodon* populated the banks of rivers and lakes, it had molars and premolars adapted to the herbivorous diet while retaining, as an archaic form, the feature of developed canines.

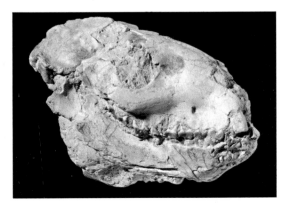

History of the horse

The horse is undoubtedly one of the classic examples of evolution. The discovery of numerous remains of horses has made it possible to reconstruct their evolutionary development. The oldest equine representative, *Eohippus*, more properly known as *Hyracotherium*, populated North America and Europe in the Eocene. Eohippus was a tiny horse compared to present-day horses. Little bigger than a hare, it lived in woods and forests. In the Oligocene, the horse grew to equal the size of a large breed of dog. Both the Eocene and the Oligocene horses put their weight on three toes on each foot. In the Miocene, *Merychyppus* took over the grasslands. Necessary transformations took place in its teeth, which had to chew tougher greenstuff, and also in its limbs. Merychyppus adapted to running by developing a big middle toe. Its two side toes did not touch the ground. In the Pliocene, with *Pliohippus*, horses assumed a form not far removed from the equine form today. It was, nevertheless, much smaller than the present-day horse. *Pliohippus* lived on the grasslands of North America, and it was in this continent that the modern horse appeared in the Quaternary. The American horse died out somewhat mysteriously. Today's stock of horses in the Americas were reintroduced into the continent by Spanish and other European colonists from the 16th century onwards.

Evolution of the horse

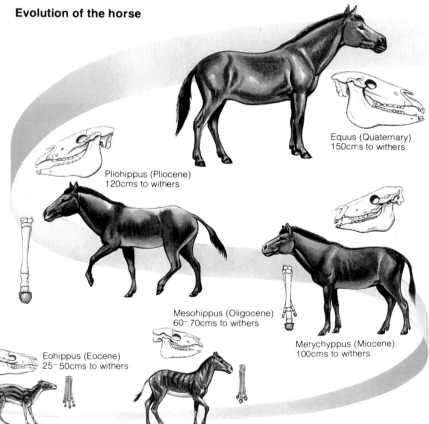

Equus (Quaternary)
150cms to withers

Pliohippus (Pliocene)
120cms to withers

Mesohippus (Oligocene)
60–70cms to withers

Merychyppus (Miocene)
100cms to withers

Eohippus (Eocene)
25–50cms to withers

Migrations of horses

Horses appeared in North America about 54 million years ago and in a series of migrations afterwards populated Euroasia and South America. The first migration to Euroasia, by way of the corridor of land which then existed in the Bering Strait, took place about 26 million years ago and involved an equine, *Anchitherium*, which was directly related to *Merychyppus*. Two further migrations across this natural bridge took place in the Pliocene and the Pleistocene.

Birds

Whereas fossil remains of birds in the Mesozoic are few and far between, there is a fair amount of evidence to indicate the presence of this group from the Cenozoic onwards. It is from this time, in fact, that birds underwent rapid evolution, and so became one of the supreme vertebrate groups. In the Cenozoic, birds existed in highly diversified and specialised forms, a state of affairs foreshadowed by the high degree of evolution already attained by birds in the Upper Cretaceous. In the Eocene, pelicans, herons and seagulls had already appeared. Their habitat, in the immediate vicinity of water, has helped to preserve their carcasses, whereas birds not closely associated with an aquatic setting, such as passerines and the other tree-dwelling birds, are only sparsely represented. This may possibly have been due chiefly to the environment in which they were living, an environment not especially conducive to the preservation of remains. Of the carnivores, the large flightless ratites underwent a major development at the start of the Cenozoic.

Ratites (or running birds)
Birds of the modern type, without teeth, are known to have existed from the Cenozoic onwards. Of these, the ratites were especially widespread. One of their descendants is *Aepyornis* (left), which lived in the Quaternary in Madagascar. Because of its height — over three metres — it is also known as 'the elephant bird'. It used to lay the biggest egg ever produced: an *Aepyornis* egg is larger than 150 hen's eggs put together.

Moa birds
The generic name Moa (pictured above) is usually given to the ratites which lived from the Pliocene until a few centuries ago in New Zealand. Having evolved in a habitat free from other competing carnivores these birds survived until the seventeenth century. Sadly they were then exterminated as a result of being hunted and having their eggs taken. Moas were completely unsuited for flying; they had practically no wings, though they did possess very well-developed hindlegs for running. The biggest of the Moas was *Dinornis* (below). The only bird of this type still surviving is the Kiwi, or *Apteryx*.

Aepyornis

Dinornis

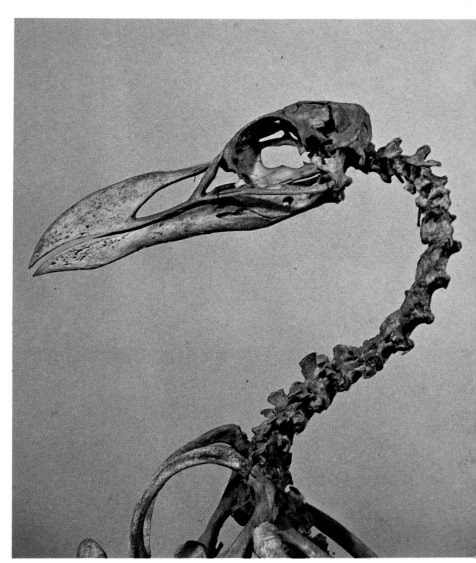

The classification of birds

Birds are currently divided into several sub-classes: the Archaeornithes comprise one genus, *Archaeopteryx*, exclusive to the Upper Jurassic in Germany. The Neornithes comprise the Hesperornis and Ichthyornis, whose beaks had teeth, and which were typical of the Upper Cretaceous. Modern birds, which appeared in the Cenozoic, however, are grouped with the Ornithurae, or birds with a primitive type of palate: this group includes the large ratites of the past, as well as modern ostriches which developed chiefly at the start of the Cenozoic. Most probably, in the absence of real opposition, they occupied the ecological niche left vacant by the disappearance of the running dinosaurs. Most of the present forms are included in the super order of Neognathae which are known to have existed from the Eocene onwards. This group comprises the forms best adapted to flying, even though this capability has been lost through adaptation in some forms. Above: a fossil feather from Eocene limestones at Monte Bolca (Verona) and a *Pelecanus intermedius* fossil egg.

The Great Auk

Similar in appearance to a penguin, the Great or Greater Auk was a flightless bird which lived in flocks of a few hundred on the coasts of Iceland and in the region of Newfoundland. Subsequently, during the glaciations of the Quaternary, the auks moved south as far as the Mediterranean, as evidenced by fossil remains found in Southern Italy. The Auk died out as a result of wholesale slaughter by hunters: the last of them died in Iceland in 1844. Right: a skeleton of an auk.

Adaptation to life in the grasslands

Phororhacos, who lived during the Miocene in South America, was ill-fitted for flight, as shown by its reduced forelegs. However, it *did* have powerful hindlegs for running in the extensive grasslands existing at that time. More than one and a half metres high, *Phororhacos* had a very developed skull and a powerful beak. *Phororhacos* is an example of adaptation by a bird to a life-style confined mainly to the ground rather than the air, in the absence of competing carnivores. Very similar to it was *Diatryma*, a bird which grew to over two metres in height and lived before *Phororhacos*, during the Eocene in North America. The illustrations below are a reconstruction of *Phororhacos*.

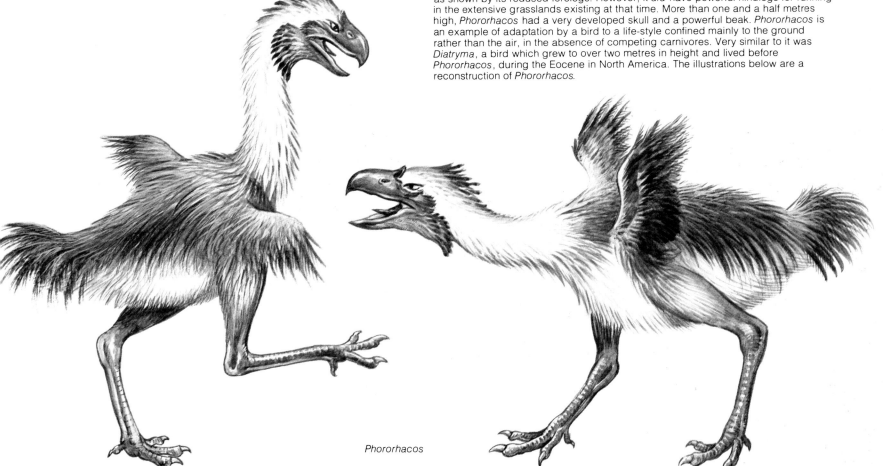

Phororhacos

The marine faunas of the Cenozoic

The marine faunas of the Cenozoic are well known today from the remarkable abundance of surviving fossil remains which reveal that, generally speaking, they closely resemble present-day fauna.

The most widely dispersed marine invertebrates of the Cenozoic Era were undoubtedly the molluscs, among them lamellibranchs, or bivalves, and the gasteropods. The plankton groups also developed considerably: in the Eocene, for example, the *Nummulites* appeared. These were foraminifera with shells as large as coins and much more developed than comparable organisms before and after them. The arthropod group featured a marked development of decapod crustaceans, including crayfish and crabs. Among the vertebrate marine fauna, there was a great diffusion of teleost fish which are still the most prominent group today. As the reptiles had done before, in the Mesozoic, the mammals went on to gain supremacy in the seas, taking over the ecological niches left vacant by marine reptiles. Cetaceans, pinnipeds and sirenians evolved rapidly, whereas, by contrast, marine reptiles such as chelonians did not undergo great evolutionary changes. The climate had much to do with this flourishing of marine life in the Cenozoic. Overall, climate was very stable throughout the Era, with fairly high mean temperatures.

Gasteropod molluscs
These picture show the closely-packed decoration on the shell of these gasteropods; this is due to the highly favourable climate, more or less constant water temperature, and good saline content and light. These conditions are comparable to those existing in present-day coral atolls.

Far left: *Fusinus*
Left: *Narona*
Above: *Murex*

Coral
A colony of corals from the Miocene, Virginia (USA), belonging to the genus *Astrangia*. During the whole of the Cenozoic, the coelenterates were characterised by widespread diffusion and a large number of species.

Pliocene fossils

A slab of clay deposited on a sea bed during the Pliocene (below) contained fossils of some of the organisms that once lived there; especially in evidence is a starfish and a lamellibranch. A worsening of the climate during the Pliocene seems to have impoverished Pliocene marine faunas, whereas faunas of preceding periods of the Cenozoic benefited from better conditions. During the Miocene, especially in Europe, the climate changed from sub-tropical to temperate.

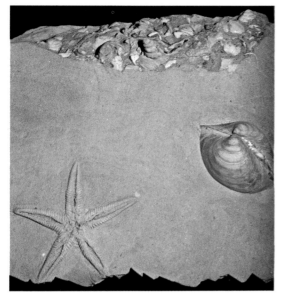

An eel from the Cenozoic

An example of *Paranguilla tigrina* (below), progenitor of modern eels, from the deposit of Monte Bolca. The fish here are preserved complete, their most minute structures being observable. In most cases the true life-size scale and shape of the animal can be gleaned from the light aureole around it.

Fish from the Eocene

The Eocene deposits in Europe are very rich in both sea and freshwater fish. Fossils of tropical freshwater fish like *Smerdis* (above) were found near Paris, while in Italy, in the Monte Bolca deposit (right and below), fish of the genuses *Mene* and *Sparnodus*, typical of a tropical marine environment, have been discovered.

A Pliocene outcrop

The photo below shows the front of a quarry where rocks dating from the Pliocene have been uncovered. Two types of sediment are easily discernible: lower down, are the 'blue clays' deposited during a phase when the sea advanced over the land, whereas further up there are the 'yellow sands' deposited by the sea during the phase when the water receded.

The Quaternary, or Neozoic ('new life') Era, began only two million years ago. We still live in it today. The Quaternary Era is characterised by the great diffusion of humans all over the world and by a cycle of glacial periods interspersed with interglacial periods when the climate was milder. During the glacial periods, a large part of the North American and European continents were covered by ice. These regions were then covered by flowers and populated by fauna of the cold-blooded type, such as the woolly rhinoceros, reindeer, caribou, cave bears and mammoths. Seas such as the Mediterranean contained organisms which had migrated from northern waters by way of the Straits of Gibraltar. During the interglacials, a warm climate and warm-blooded animals arrived; hippopotami and elephant replaced the cold-blooded fauna, while in the seas the fauna from the coasts of Africa were populating the Mediterranean. In the Quaternary there were five big glaciations, known as Gunz, Mindel, Riss and Würm from geographical names in the Northern Alps.

The Quaternary Era

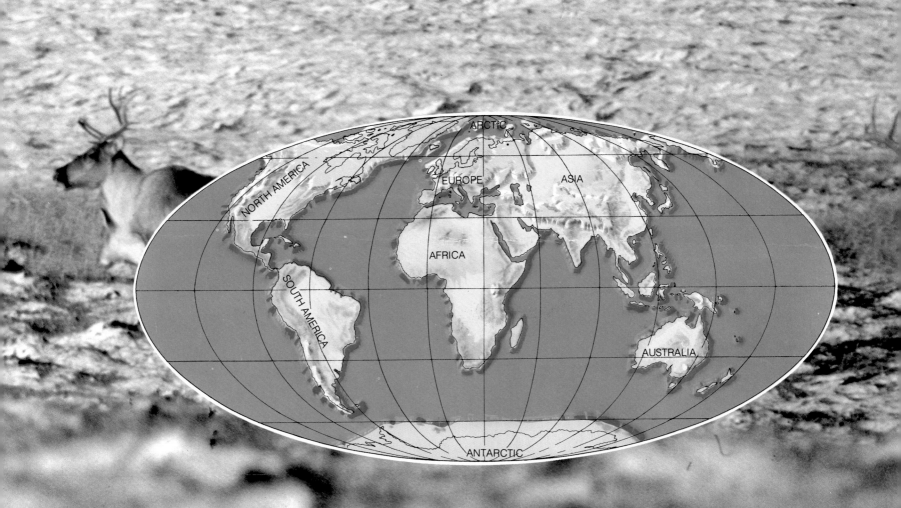

Quaternary fauna

During the Quaternary Era, the geography of the Earth was much the same as it is today. However, the climate was very different, being marked by alternating warm and cold periods. These variations in climate resulted in major migrations: in the warmer interglacial periods, the typical warm-belt faunas were driven north, whereas in the colder, glacial periods the faunas from the cold belts came south. This explains how hippopotami, elephants and rhinoceri were supplanted, as the climate changed, by mammoths, woolly rhinoceri and bears. The fossil remains found in sediments from rivers and lakes in the European Quaternary demonstrate this alternating climate. In London, for instance, remains of elephants, hippopotami, cervids and felids have been found to show that in the interglacial periods they populated the luxuriant banks of the Thames.

Tar pools of North America
This magnificent skull belongs to a sabre-toothed tiger, the *Smilodon*, a carnivore from the Quaternary whose remains were unearthed at Rancho La Brea near Los Angeles, in the United States. In this area the release of hydrocarbons from the subsoil caused real tar pools to form. The pools were swelled by rainwater, so that when the animals of the plain came here to drink, they became trapped in the soft viscous soil. Helpless, they were then attacked by other carnivores and birds which in their turn were engulfed by the tar. Among numerous Rancho La Brea fossils is a skeleton of *Glossotherium* (below), a tree-dwelling three-toed sloth which migrated from South America.

In the Siberian ice
In the ice of Siberia perfectly preserved carcasses have been found of mammoths who populated the Siberian plains during the Quaternary. The bodies of these creatures have been so well preserved over several thousand years, that when they emerged from the ice, wolves were attracted to the meat. Below: The remains of Siberian mammoths at the Museum in Jakutsk.

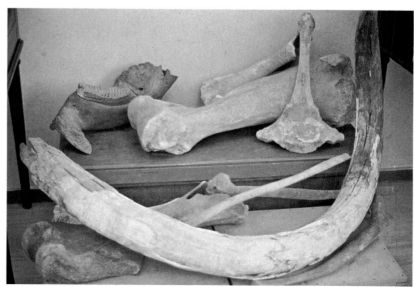

Mammoth

A splendid skull of a mammoth, a woolly elephant which inhabited the plains during the glacial phases of the Quaternary. Smaller in size than an African elephant, it has a body covered in thick bristly hair and enormous tusks which were very useful for digging into the snow to pull up the plants on which it fed.

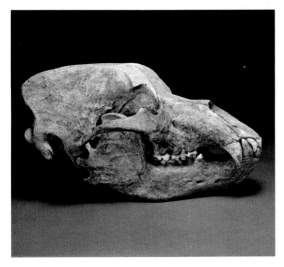

Cave bear

The powerful skull of *Ursus spelaeus* (left), which lived in the foothills of mountains throughout Europe. This was the direct competitor of primitive man who fought with it to gain control of the caves.

Continental fauna of the Plio-Quaternary

Discoveries made in the Valdarno region of Tuscany have provided firm evidence for our knowledge of continental fauna of the period from the Upper Pliocene to the Lower Quaternary. In this area there was a small lake, the bed of which revealed deposits of several vertebrate carcasses. These were preserved in a series of sand and clay layers. Featured on this page: the skeleton of *Anancus arvernensis*, a gigantic proboscidean (left), and *Ursus minimus* (below right) which belong to the Upper Pliocene; *Sus strozzi* (centre right), *Canis arnensis* (above right) and *Leptobos etruscus* (above), a bovid measuring 70cms between the horns, were found in sediments deposited during the Quaternary. The Valdarno probably looked quite different compared to the present day; a river ran into this lake, and horses, hyenas, deer, hippopotami and rhinoceri lived in the rich vegetation along its banks.

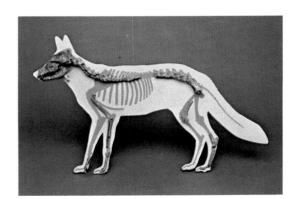

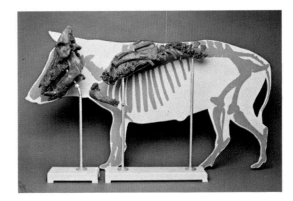

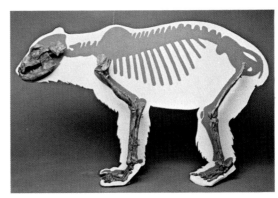

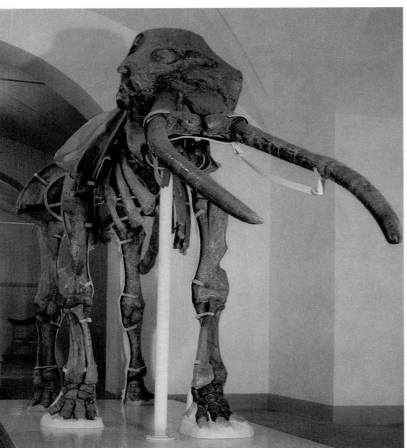

The Ice Ages

The Quaternary Era begins with the period called Pleistocene, characterised by alternately cool and warm climatic periods. These fluctuations in weather had great influence both on the morphology of dry land and on the distribution and evolution of living organisms. This applied especially to continental fauna. Since the end of the Mesozoic Era, the Earth's climate had grown generally colder. In the Quaternary, a combination of factors gave rise to a series of very cold periods or glaciations: one of these factors was the appearance, towards the end of the Cenozoic Era, of the Panama isthmus which joined South to North America. This blocked the exchange of equatorial waters between the Pacific and Atlantic Oceans. However, the main cause of climatic fluctuations was pinpointed in 1938, by the astronomer Milankovitch, as the variation in supply of solar energy to the Earth's surface. This variation was caused by changes in a number of astronomical parameters, such as the orbit of the elliptical plane, the axis of the ecliptic and the precession of the equinoxes, which vary cyclically with a recurrence of 93,000 years, 41,000 years and 21,000 years respectively. Therefore the varying distance and inclination of the Earth in relation to the Sun meant a difference in the supply of solar energy reaching Earth. Consequently the general climate varies by getting warmer or colder.

Glaciations in Europe
The map below shows in greater detail the situation of Europe during the glacial periods. The northern parts were covered in ice, while in south-central Europe the glaciers covered only the mountain ranges of the Alps and the Pyrenees, spreading down until they reached the lowlands. The areas of central Europe which were free of ice were covered by the type of vegetation found in areas of tundra with the sub-soil iced over throughout the year (permafrost).

POSTGLACIAL

WÜRM

RISS-WÜRM
INTERGLACIAL

RISS

MINDEL-RISS
INTERGLACIAL

MINDEL

GUNZ-MINDEL
INTERGLACIAL

GUNZ

PREGLACIAL
WARM

COLD

Duration of period about 1 million years

Glaciations
In the last million years or so, there have been four main glacial periods in Europe, starting with Gunz, then going on to Mindel, Riss and Würm. These names are taken from villages and rivers in the North-West Alps. Between one glacial period and the next, there were warmer periods called interglacials, which were named after the two glaciations before and after them, i.e. the Gunz–Mindel interglacial, the Mindel–Riss interglacial and the Riss–Würm interglacial. The Pleistocene came to an end after the Würm glaciation. The postglacial Holocene then began; this is the period in which we are presently living. In North America, and also in New Zealand, there were four known glaciations. This confirms that the climatic variations of the Pleistocene involved the whole world. In the diagram (left) you can see the drop or rise in temperature over the last million years: glacial periods are shown in blue, interglacials in red.

Ice-caps
Large ice-caps are currently found only in the polar regions whereas on the highest mountain ranges permanent glaciers are on a limited scale. During the glacial periods, the stretches of ice were much more extensive than they are today. In the map (above) you can see how enormous stretches of ice covered most of the northern parts of America, Asia and Europe.

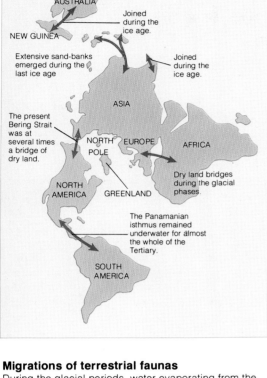

Migrations of terrestrial faunas
During the glacial periods, water evaporating from the sea fell again as rain and helped swell the large ice-caps. Consequently, it is reckoned that on several occasions the sea level dropped to as much as 90 metres below present level. As a result, the sea beds were no longer submerged and so formed natural bridges between territories which had before been separated by the sea. This made it possible for terrestrial fauna to migrate. The phenomenon occurred between North America and Asia, Africa and Europe, and between the islands of Southeast Asia.

Island fauna
With the variation in sea level and the emergence of new territories, some of the animals driven back by the advance of the polar ice-caps were able to find new areas to live. Either they occupied the land which had risen above sea level or used it as 'bridges' to gain access to areas otherwise out of reach. This state of affairs had important consequences for the mammals on the islands who are showing interesting signs of evolution in the Quaternary. When the sea level rose again, those fauna which crossed these natural 'bridges' to occupy the islands were cut off from fauna which had remained on the continent. Their evolution therefore diverged. In particular herbivorous mammals found in dwarf forms on the islands of the Mediterranean grew to a great size on the continent: the little elephant of Sicily (above right); dwarf elephants also inhabited Malta and the Indonesian archipelago. Conversely, mammals which were small-sized on the continent developed giant forms on the islands, such as the large rodents that lived on the Mediterranean islands during the Pleistocene.

Migrations by sea
The map (left) gives an outline of the route taken by typical cold-zone marine faunas in order to enter the Mediterranean (blue arrow) during the glacial periods. It also shows the matching migrations of fauna from tropical seas in the interglacial periods (red arrow) during which the waters of the Mediterranean became warmer than they are today.

'Warm' and 'cold' guests in the Mediterranean
The Pleistocene sedimentary marine deposits found in the Mediterranean area have a very interesting fauna content. The marine Pleistocene is in fact distinguished by the presence of molluscs which are commonly called 'warm guests' and 'cold guests'.

During the interglacial phases the temperature was rising and animals which normally lived on the coasts of Africa, like the *Strombus* (left), crossed the Straits of Gibraltar and spread through the Mediterranean, which offered more favourable climatic conditions. During the glacial periods, on the other hand, the Mediterranean played host to animals which today are typical of the coasts of Nordic countries. For instance, the bivalve *Arctica islandica* or 'Arctic Visitor' (right) moved by way of Gibraltar to the marine territories abandoned by the warm-blooded fauna which had not managed to survive the severe climatic conditions.

The terrestrial landscape
Alternate warm and cold periods had significant consequences for the morphology and landscapes of the land above sea level: glaciers moving down from the mountains caused powerful erosion in the valleys they crossed, hollowing them out to leave a distinctive U-shaped profile (right). They also brought down a considerable mass of detritus which went to form the characteristic morainic hills. The winds sweeping the desolate heathlands, that were devoid of vegetation, created accumulations of very fine sands or loess. This occasionally occurred on an enormous scale, as can be found in China. During the interglacial periods, on the other hand, many now temperate regions probably had a landscape very similar in vegetation and fauna to that now found only in the tropics (left).

The oldest hominids
The remains of the oldest hominids have been discovered in Africa. Olduvai Gorge (above) in Tanzania became especially famous following discoveries made there by Louis Leakey, his wife Dorothy and son Richard. Other sites well known for their hominid remains are in Kenya and particularly in Ethiopia. Here, in the Awash valley, the remains have recently been found of the earliest *Australopithecus* yet known, dating back about four million years. Left: an *Australopithecus* skull from Olduvai.

The origins of Man

The origin of modern Man is still for the most part swathed in mystery. Even though the common characteristics of the genus *Homo* and primates like the gorilla and the chimpanzee are obvious and well known, the phylogenetic process which led to the appearance of the human species is not yet fully understood.

According to the most recent discoveries, in Ethiopia, it seems that some four million years ago a primate, known today as *Austra-*

lopithecus (Southern Man) was able to stand upright. This is regarded as the first step towards the development of humans. The earliest classifiable forms within the genus *Homo* belong to a group called *Homo habilis*, who lived in Africa between two million and one and a half million years ago. *Homo habilis* was the first creature to fashion stone tools, a sign of intelligence. About a million years ago, *Homo erectus* appeared. Remains of *Homo erectus* have been found in Africa,

Asia and Europe; carbonised remains found at fossil sites reveals that *Homo erectus* was the first to use fire. The appearance of early types of *Homo sapiens* dates back perhaps 250,000 years. We know a number of known sub-species of *Homo Sapiens* are extinct, including Neanderthal Man (*H. sapiens neanderthalensis*) or Cro-Magnon Man, who was the nearer of the two to modern Man.

Ramapithecus
11 mill. years ago

Australopithecus
3½ mill. years ago

Homo habilis
1½ mill. years ago

Homo erectus
500,000 years ago

Homo sapiens
200,000 years ago

Homo Sapiens Sapiens
(Modern Man)

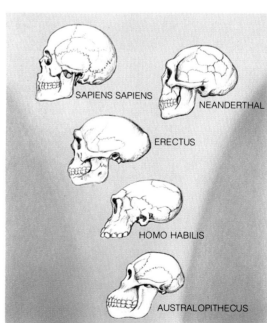

SAPIENS SAPIENS

NEANDERTHAL

ERECTUS

HOMO HABILIS

AUSTRALOPITHECUS

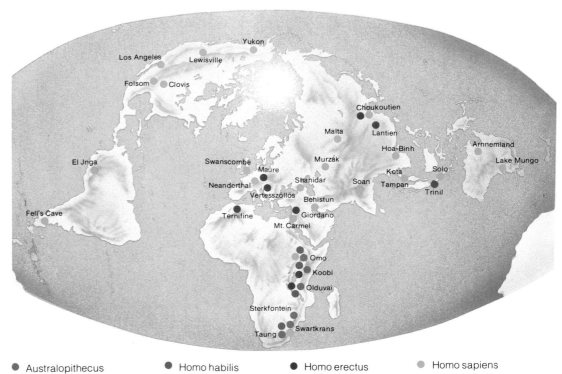

● Australopithecus   ● Homo habilis   ● Homo erectus   ● Homo sapiens

The first tool-makers

Homo habilis was probably the first maker of very primitive stone implements such as scrapers and choppers (above) as well as tool-making tools.

The stone tools made by *Homo erectus* are much more advanced. Together with his remains, well-worked handaxes and cutting tools have been unearthed. Below: an axe of the so-called Acheulian type, found at Azir (Algeria).

Remains of hominids in the world

A map showing the geographical distribution of the main discoveries of fossil hominids in the world (above) and another (left) with the main European sites. Note how the oldest hominid remains (*Australopithecus* and *Homo habilis*) have been found in Africa, in particular along the break in the Earth's crust known as the Rift Valley.

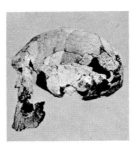

Skull '1470'

A famous hominid find is the skull known as '1470' which Richard Leakey discovered on the banks of Lake Turkana (Kenya). Its age is still in dispute. It had a then remarkable 800cc cranial capacity.

Remains of *H. sapiens*

Fossils afford little information concerning the period between 500,000 and 250,000 years ago, during which the first examples of *Homo sapiens* appeared. Well known among those which *have* been found are the Sternheim remains in Germany, and remains at Swanscombe in England, which belonged to humans with about 1300cc cranial capacity. In the Arago cave, in France, remains of *Homo sapiens* have been discovered dating back about 250,000 years. These finds contain some very primitive features; there are similar features in a number of skulls found in Africa, particularly those unearthed by Richard Leakey in 1967 by the River Omo (Kenya) which contain transitional characteristics between *H. erectus* and *H. sapiens*. In Europe, during the last glaciation, there lived a primitive *H. sapiens* known as Neanderthal Man, whose connexions with modern man are still undetermined. One of the first examples of modern man is Cro-Magnon Man who appeared in Europe about 40,000 years ago. Right: a Cro-Magnon skull from the cave of La Chapelle (France).

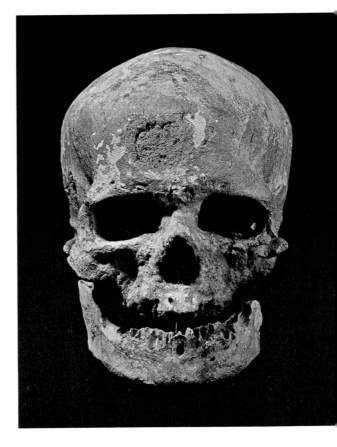

Living fossils

On the 22nd December, 1938, off the eastern seaboard of South Africa, a fishing-boat picked up a strange fish, more than one and a half metres long, with unusual fleshy flippers. The creature was taken to the small Museum of Natural History·at East London (South Africa), where the curator, Miss Courtenay-Latimer, realised this was an exceptional find. She was, however, unable to classify it and so sent it to an expert, Professor Smith. To his surprise and excitement Smith recognised the strange fish as a coelacanth, i.e. a representative of a very ancient group of fish believed to have died out some 70 million years before! As a mark of appreciation to Miss Latimer for this great find, Professor Smith called the fish by the generic name of Latimeria. Researches were continued by French zoologists and, on the strength of fresh discoveries, much came to be known about Latimeria and its way of life. It lived in the Mozambique Channel and around the Comores archipelago, at depths between 150 and 800 metres. It was carnivorous and ovoviviparous (that is, its embryos grew in the female's womb). However, the most spectacular feature of the coelacanth was without doubt its matching flippers which were, in effect, a very early foreshadowing of the limbs of land vertebrates. Latimeria is thus one of the 'living fossils' which has aroused enormous interest among zoologists. 'Living fossils' are present-day organisms which represent the residue of very old faunas and floras. These organisms have survived with characteristics almost unaltered for millions of years. A living fossil is evidently a unique chance for scientists to study in depth the structures of organisms from the distant biological past of the Earth. All the more so, because these may be structures not preserved in conventional fossil evidence, or at times only partly preserved, as in the case of soft parts of the body. Latimeria is one of the best known and most interesting living fossils because of its close connection with crossopterygian fish which gave rise to the amphibians. There are also numerous organisms, in the present-day fauna and flora, which can be regarded as living fossils; one of the best known among them is Neopilina, the only living representative of a class of molluscs, the monoplacophora. Monoplacophora were thought to have been extinct for 350 million years before 1957, when Neopilina was caught off the coast of Costa Rica.

The Metasequoia
In 1945, in China, the botanist T. Kan noticed an unusual conifer which, unlike other pine-trees, lost its leaves in winter. Experts afterwards studying the strange plant discovered that it was identical to a fossil form found shortly before in Japan. Today this plant, metasequoia, or dawn redwood (above and left) is widespread in parks and gardens.

The gingko
The *Gingko biloba* is the sole surviving species of a very old group of gymnosperms which died out 100 million years ago. At the present moment, *Gingko biloba* is known exclusively in the cultivated state (above). In fact it seems that *Gingko biloba* was saved from extinction by being cultivated since very ancient times. It is a slender tree with cone-shaped foliage and distinctive finely veined fan-shaped leaves (right) reminiscent of maidenhair fern leaves. The trees are sexually distinct and can thus be classed as male or female. The male plant produces pollen in pendent or overhanging spikes, while the female grows ovules the size of a cherry complete with pulp and stone.

The Nautilus

Another famous living fossil is the *Nautilus*, which is currently found in the Indian Ocean. Once plentiful in the seas of the past, it is today the only cephalopod mollusc which has an outer shell; this shell is divided inside into a series of chambers which the creature uses as a flotation chamber. Like submarines, the Nautilus fills, then empties, its chamber with gas. Nautiluses were very widespread until the start of the Mesozoic Era, when they went into a progressive decline while the ammonites were enjoying an evolutionary flowering. However, unlike the ammonites, which died out completely at the end of the Mesozoic Era, nautiluses survive to this day. Above: a fossil nautilus; above right: shells of present-day nautiluses.

The monitor lizard

The monitor lizard (right) is a reptile from the same group as the lizards and iguanas, the *Lacertidae*, to which numerous fossil forms belong, including the giant mosasaurs of the Cretaceous Period. Various species can be found in Africa, Southern Asia and Australia; monitor lizards are basically carnivores: they feed on other vertebrates and their eggs. The monitor lizard from the island of Komodo can measure more than four metres.

The Limulus

The *Limulus* exists today in six species which live along the Atlantic coasts of the United States and along Indopacific coasts from India to Japan. These few species represent the only survivors of the xiphosurans — aquatic arthropods closely related to the Giant Water Scorpions. Arthropods were exclusive to the Palaeozoic seas and sometimes reached enormous size. The first real *Limulus* appeared about 170 million years ago and has barely altered since that time. Above: a present-day *Limulus*; right: a *Limulus* in Jurassic limestone at Solnhofen (Bavaria).

The sphenodont

Sphenodon punctatus, or *Tuatara*, or *Hatteria*, is the sole surviving species of the reptile order of Rhynchocephalians, which developed during the Mesozoic. *Sphenodon punctatus* lives in some of the islands off the coast of New Zealand, where it was recorded for the first time by Captain James Cook in the 1770s. It is a lizard up to 70cms long and feeds on small creatures and eggs which it hunts at night. By day, *Sphenodon punctatus* remains in its nest or underwater. It sometimes shelters in the nests of petrels, and can live more than 100 years. In the nineteenth century it was believed to be near extinction, but today it is out of danger. Right: *Homeosaurus*, a Jurassic rhynchopcephalian; below right: a modern sphenodont.

Curiosities of Palaeontology

The discovery of fossil materials by the very early peoples gave rise to a large number of myths and legends. Fossils acquired supernatural or medicinal powers and a fantastic web of myth was woven around them. For instance, during the Middle Ages, five or six centuries ago, the fossil skull of a woolly rhinoceros (right) found near the town of Klagenfurt in Austria led to the erection of the statue seen below. The people of Klagenfurt had no knowledge of rhinoceri, and so concluded that the remains belonged to a dragon which had once lived and died in the area. The statue is possibly one of the first known examples of palaeontological reconstruction.

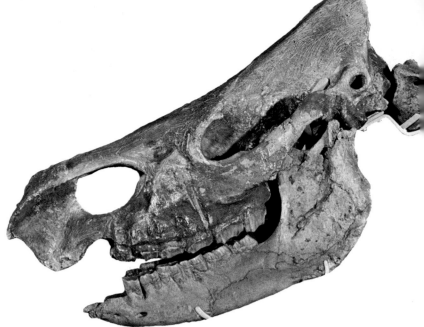

The skeleton featured on the right is the remains of a giant salamander from the Miocene, more than a metre long, found in the Canton of Soleure in Switzerland. The man who discovered it in 1726, the Swiss geologist and doctor Canon J. J. Scheuchzer, believed these were the remains of a man who had perished during the Biblical Flood. Scheuchzer therefore named him *Homo diluvii testis*, that is, man, a witness of the Flood.'

Some sixty years later, however, the famous palaeontologist Baron Georges Cuvier showed that this was an amphibian. Scheuchzer's original diagnosis was one of the most notable mistakes in the history of palaeontology.

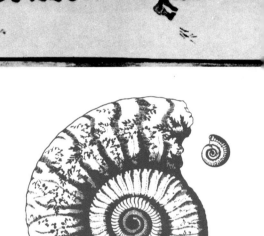

Isolated sharks' teeth are frequently found in China's Tertiary soils (above). The ancient Chinese believed them to be dragons' teeth lost when the monsters chomped rocks in fits of rage.

Belemnites (below), inner shells of Mesozoic cephalopods, were in ancient times thought to be the points of lightning flashes which became stuck into the ground.

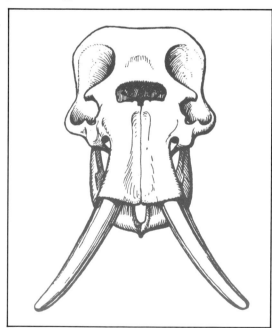

The remains of elephants discovered in a number of caves in Sicily roused the imagination of the discoverers in early times. Not knowing anything about these powerful mammals, they believed the remains belonged to the one-eyed giants known in Ancient Greek mythology as Cyclops.

Nineteenth century satirists tended to lampoon the most famous and talked-about personalities: here is a distinguished palaeontologist giving a lecture to an extinct mammal in his laboratory.

This early representation of an ammonite (above) was described and drawn by the Italian physician Michele Mercati in 1717. The name ammonite derives from the Ancient Egyptian god Ammon, who was portrayed with horns resembling the shell of these cephalopods.

Classifying Fossils

Systematics is the science of classification; that is, the science which studies the hierarchy of the types of organisms. On the basis of these types, groups of animals and plants are divided into categories called *systematic units*. The purpose of systematic studies is to arrange the orders of animals and plants so as to form a basic knowledge of organisms which in their turn provide a starting-point for more in-depth studies, in evolutionism, ecology and biogeography. It would, in fact, be impossible to carry out an evolutionary study on a group of animals unless the organisms belonging to it had first been identified, its possible sub-groups established, and characteristics singled out which enable a given number of organisms to be put together in that group.

Since fossils are the remains of once living animals and plants, the palaeontologist has to treat them exactly as though he were dealing with creatures now living. In making his classification he relies greatly on the information offered by the living world, which is, of course, richer in material. The palaeontologist must take account of the individual variability of the organisms and of the groups, and of all the aspects peculiar to each organism which are not easy to observe in the fossil material but can easily be identified in living groups.

The basic systematic unit is the *species*. This unique natural category can be defined as a collection of organisms potentially or actually capable of reproducing by crossbreeding. This definition of the species naturally takes us a long way away from palaeontology, for the species, in this sense, cannot be verified from the inert sort of material the palaeontologist has at his disposal. Defining a palaeontological species is therefore a highly complex business, for two reasons. First, there is no chance of checking. Secondly, the time factor is of major significance in palaeontology — something which does not affect studies on living material.

Whereas the biologist has a partial view of the living world which is confined to a single period of time, the palaeontologist has a much broader canvas. He sees every group of animals and plants in the different periods of their history with a global vision in a temporal, and therefore evolutionary, sense. Where biological species are definable only in a spatial sense, the palaeontological, also called *chronospecies*, can be defined in a temporal sense as well. Thus, the palaeontological species is variable in space and in time, while the biological one is variable only in space.

It is, therefore, difficult for palaeontology to set limits to species. In a spatial sense, that is within each time period, definition is fairly straightforward, even though somewhat subjective through lack of corroborative evidence. However, sub-division in terms of time is *purely* subjective. The palaeontologist has to deal with groups which are in a state of continuous gradual change through time, and this does not permit him to establish, except arbitrarily, systematic subdivisions within the line of evolution.

At a higher level than that of species, systematic units are not based on biologically demonstrable characteristics and are thus dependent on subjective or traditional interpretations. This is why species are grouped under *genera*, genera under *families*, families in *orders*, orders in *classes*, and classes in *types* or *phyla* (plural of the Latin *phylum*). Beside the main categories mentioned, there are numerous other systematic categories; these are, for example, the superfamily, the sub-type, the super-order, the sub-order, and so on.

Systematics is a science governed by strict laws, which have to be followed by all researchers if they are to avoid the confusion which would inevitably arise if each were to use their own nomenclature. The laws of systematics are gathered in an *International Code of Zoological Nomenclature* published in 1961 and followed by all systematicians. The Code lays down the methods to employ in order to use the correct nomenclature for organisms, to give them a consistent description, and so on.

Every organism, animal or plant, is defined by a double Latin name in which the first part represents the genus and the second the species to which it belongs. The generic name has to be written with a capital letter, whereas the specific name is always with a small letter. This is the case even when the latter is dedicated to a scholar and bears his or her name. The giant salamander mistaken by Canon Scheuchzer for 'a man', a witness of the flood (see page 80), was later named after him as Andrias scheuchzeri. After the scientific name comes that of the inventor who was the first to define and describe the species, and the year in which that description was published for the first time; this makes it possible to refer back fairly easily to the original mention in print. The scientific name of the lion, *Panthera leo* thus becomes *Panthera leo* (Linnaeus, 1758). The name of the inventor and publication date are put there in brackets with good reason: they indicate that the inventor attributed the species to a different genus from the one in which it is classified today. Linnaeus classified the species *leo* in the 'cat' genus *Felis* and not in the genus *Panthera*. The latter was introduced later as a result of more advanced systematic research.

The complete classification of a lion reads as follows:

species	*leo*
genus	*Panthera*
family	*Felidae*
order	*Carnivora*
class	*Mammalia*
sub-type	*Vertebrata*
type	*Chordata*

or: 'the lion is a carnivorous vertebrate mammal of the feline (cat) family'. The scientific names of the tiger, *Panthera tigris* (Linnaeus, 1758) and leopard, *Panthera pardus* (Linnaeus, 1758), show that lion, tiger and leopard all belong to the same genus.

Sometimes in the course of classification the genus, but not the species, of a certain organism, can be defined. The generic name is followed by the letters sp: or sp.ind: which mean 'indeterminate species'. If the species is uncertain, a question mark is put before the specific name. Either that or the letters cf. 'compare', to show that one can go no further than simply comparing the animal with an already known species.

Take the example of the lion again. If a zoologist of limited expertise cannot define a lion once it has been captured, he would simply write it down as *Felis* sp., in other words a feline whose species cannot be better identified; if on the other hand he wrote *Felis* cf. *leo*, this would mean he was not sure he had found a lion, even though the animal very closely resembled a lion.

What follows is a systematic summary of the groups of plants and animals which have fossil representatives. The list does not go below the level of *order* and in the case of each group only the main characteristics and limits of diffusion in time have been given.

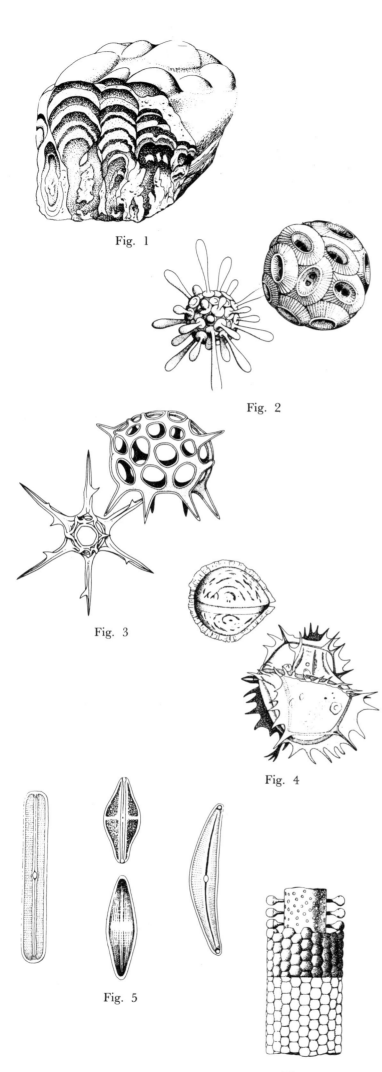

Fig. 1

Fig. 2

Fig. 3

Fig. 4

Fig. 5

Fig. 6

PLANTS

This summary does not include fungi and lichens which are very rare in the fossil state.

Type **Schizophytes**

Class Schizophyceae

Schizophyceae, also called blue-green algae or Cyanophyceae, are organisms made up of filaments of cells, with a resistant sheath, capable of fixing the calcium carbonate content in water and thus forming calcareous deposits. These concentric deposits, due to the activity of the schizophyceae, are known in the fossil state from the Archaeozoic era onwards. In those very ancient seas, they constituted calcareous reefs over a considerable area. These fossil structures are called stromatolites (fig. 1).

Class Schizomycetes

To the class *Schizomycetes* belong micro-organisms commonly known by the name bacteria. They are very simple, colourless organisms and are usually lacking in chlorophyll.

The fact that bacteria existed in past geological eras is indirectly indicated because the activity of these organisms is believed to cause the formation of a number of sedimentary deposits of iron, limestone and phosphates. Fossil bacteria have been observed at first hand in deposits of fossil carbon, in some very ancient rocks, and in the excrement and soft teguments of a number of animals preserved in the fossil state.

Eobacterium, the oldest known organism has been classified with the bacteria: it was found in rocks of the Fig Tree formation in the Eastern Transvaal which were more than three thousand million years old.

Type **Chrysophyta**

Class Chrysophyceae

Two groups of very common micro-organisms in the fossil state have been attributed to the class Chrysophyceae, the coccolithophores and the silicoflagellates. The coccolithophores (fig. 2), currently very widespread in warm seas, are microscopic flagellate cells covered in minute variously shaped calcareous plates. These small plates are preserved in the fossil state by being deposited on the sea bed after the destruction of the cell where they help to form calcareous deposits. Coccolithophores are known from the Palaeozoic: in the Cretaceous they become so plentiful that the Craie in the Paris basin is composed almost exclusively of the remains of these organisms.

Less widespread are the silicoflagellates (fig. 3). These planktonic micro-organisms were typical of cold seas, and were made up of a siliceous skeleton consisting of two reticular-shaped valves. They appeared in the Upper Cretaceous and were especially widespread during the Cenozoic Era.

Type **Pyrrophyta**

Class Dinophyceae

Dinoflagellates (fig. 4) are attributed to the class Dinophyceae. They are planktonic organisms which currently live in freshwater and sea-water settings, and possess a resistant theca adorned with prickles and long appendages varied in shape. This theca is preserved by fossilisation. Dinoflagellates are known to go back as far as the Palaeozoic Era.

Type **Bacillariophyta**

Class Bacillariophyceae

To this class belong micro-organisms with a small siliceous shell that live in marine waters and in freshwater settings in cold regions, and are known by the name siliceous algae, or diatoms (fig. 5). The siliceous shell of the diatoms, which are highly variable in form and dimensions, have contributed to the formation of sedimentary accumulations in lagoons or lakes.

These rocks, which are white and friable, and consist almost exclusively of the shells of these organisms, are called fossil flour, tripoli or diatomite.

The oldest known diatoms have been found in sediments dating from the Lower Jurassic.

Type **Phaeophyta**

Class Phaeophyceae

Phaeophyceae are brown algae, presently widespread both in the sea and, in a number of cases, in continental freshwater areas. They are little known as fossils; some large-scale fragments attributed to them came from Silurian and Devonian soils. These are fragments of the stem, almost a metre in diameter, and were originally thought to be trunks of giant conifers.

Type **Rhodophyta**

Class Rhodophyceae

These red algae are now to be found in all seas. In the past, the solenophoraceae, which lived from the Silurian to the Cretaceous, and the corallinaceae, which appeared in the Cretaceous and are still in existence today, assumed notable importance. Under the microscope, they appear to be made up of radial threads of small cells and taken as a whole they form nodular masses or encrustations. In the seas of the past, they helped to build up underwater reefs which were either isolated or linked to coral constructions.

Type **Chlorophyta**

Class Chlorophyceae

Chlorophyceae are green algae which now live in tropical seas and freshwater settings. In the past they played a very important part in the building up of calcareous reefs, either in isolation from or together with other builder organisms, such as the coelenterates. The most interesting groups from a palaeontological point of view are the Codiaceae and the Dasycladaceae, both of which appeared in the Silurian.

The Codiaceae are plants formed of branched tubes divided into tiny joints superimposed on each other and covered in small holes. The Dasycladaceae (fig. 6) are microscopic algae consisting of a branched stem whose outer parts can fix calcium carbonate in water and thus construct a kind of exterior calcareous skeleton.

The considerable abundance of these algae greatly contributed to the building of the coral reefs of the Triassic in northern Italy.

Type **Pteridophyta**

Pteridophyta are plants without flowers or seeds which reproduce by means of spores. They appeared in the Silurian and were the basis of plant life on land for a large part of the Palaeozoic Era. They are credited with the conquest of the subaereal environment together with the group of psilophytes.

Class Psilopsida

The group of psilophytes, the first terrestrial plants, belong to this class, along with a number of types still in existence today. They appeared in the Silurian and became particularly widespread in the Devonian. They were modest-scale plants, consisting basically of an underground stem without roots, which produced vertical aereal stems divided dichotomously (fig. 7).

Class Lycopsida

This broad class, nowadays represented by a few herbaceous forms (lycopods), include some of the most spectacular plants of the past which in the Carboniferous — their period of peak development — could grow as high as 30m. These are the lepidodendrons and sigillariae which in the Palaeozoic — from the Devonian to the Permian — formed thick forests bordering the marshes and lakes. The lepidodendrons (fig. 8) consisted of a trunk with numerous branches at the top, whereas the sigillarias (fig. 9) had very little in the way of branches. The whole stele was covered by special microphyllous leaves. These were narrow and elongated and left a cicatrice when they fell. The classification of these plants is now based on the shape of that cicatrice, which is invariably well preserved in the fossil state.

Class Sphenopsida

Several Palaeozoic tree forms able to grow to considerable heights (fig. 10) have been attributed to this class, which is currently represented by small herbaceous plants (equisetales). These are calamophyton which lived with their base below the water in marshland and helped to form the great luxuriant swamp forests of the Carboniferous Period. These ancient plants consisted of a trunk made up of a succession of joints separated by nodes which came apart easily. The trunk ended in a tuft of pseudoleaves, while tiny little leaves called 'articulai', from the Latin for 'knob' or 'knot', grew on the trunk nodes.

Class Pteropsida

These are ferns, still very plentiful today, which became very widespread in the Palaeozoic, both in small-size herbaceous forms and in arborescent or tree forms, which grew to considerable heights (fig. 11). They were the first plants to grow real leaves. This meant they could be further removed from water, and so constitute an important part of the composition of the forests that grew up in dry places during the Carboniferous.

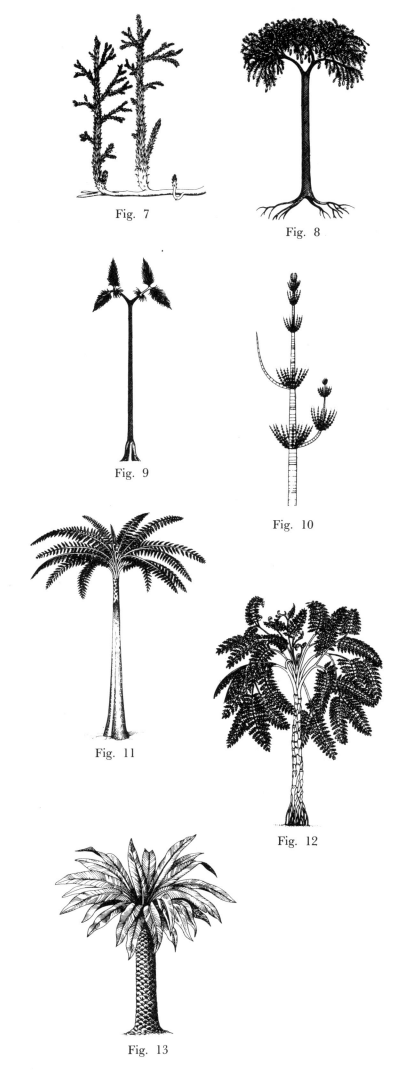

Fig. 7

Fig. 8

Fig. 9

Fig. 10

Fig. 11

Fig. 12

Fig. 13

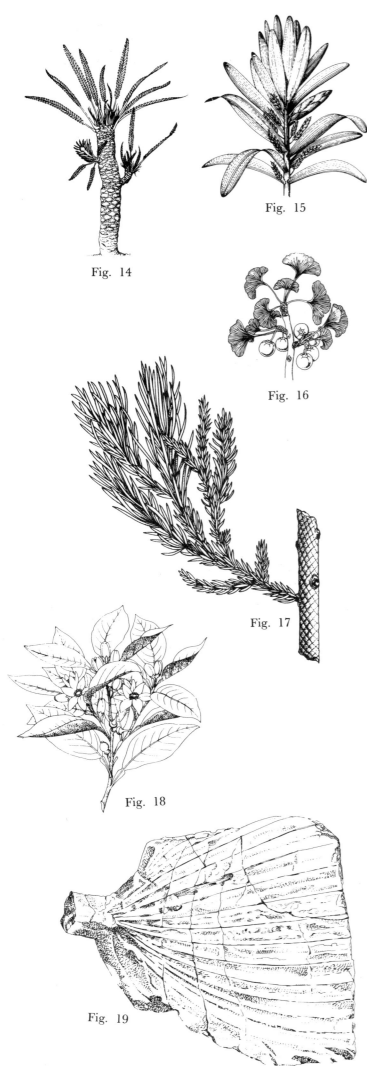

Fig. 15

Fig. 14

Fig. 16

Fig. 17

Fig. 18

Fig. 19

Type **Spermatophyta**

The Spermatophytes are the most evolved of plants in that, unlike all preceding plants, they reproduced by means of seeds.

Sub-type **Gymnospermae**

Gymnosperms are plants that do not reproduce by spores but have 'naked' seeds, i.e. not protected by an outer covering. They appeared in the Devonian Period.

Class Pteridospermae

Pteridosperms (fig. 12) are now completely extinct. As plants, they were very similar to ferns, but differed from them by having real seeds. They appeared in the Devonian, and became a substantial part of the vegetation in the Carboniferous. After this period they took on an increasingly important role, and in the Permian characterised the two big provinces of flora distribution: the pteridosperm flora of the northern continents with cycads and cordaites; and the pteridosperm flora of Gondwanaland, of the widespread genus *Glossopteris*, which is easy to recognise from its oval leaf. Pteridosperms died out at the end of the Palaeozoic Era.

Class Cycadales

Cycadales appeared in the Carboniferous and are now represented by about a hundred tropical plant species which closely resemble palm-trees. They consist of a simple trunk, without branches, which is cylindrical, covered in scales and culminates in a tuft of palm-like leaves (fig. 13).

Cycadales had their greatest development in the Triassic and Jurassic.

Class Bennettitales

These appeared in the Permian and their major development took place in the Jurassic and Cretaceous. They died out at the start of the Cenozoic Era.

Bennettitales are similar to the cycadales, with a cylindrical branchless trunk and a tuft of pinnate leaves at the top which could once grow as long as 3m. They are, however, distinct from the Cycadales in having a flower with male and female reproductive organs. Many scholars see the Bennettitales as the group from which the angiosperms derived (fig. 14).

Class Cordaitales

Cordaitales are primitive gymnosperms which appeared in the Devonian and disappeared at the end of the Palaeozoic Era. They were able to grow as high as 30 or 40m.; they had slender trunks with leafy branches. The leaves were elongated and were inserted spirally on the branches. They had parallel venation and could be as long as a metre (fig. 15). In general, Cordaitales probably resembled conifers.

Class Ginkgoales

The ginkgoales, of which today a single species: *Gingko biloba* (fig. 16) remains, appeared in the Carboniferous, and reached their peak of development in the Jurassic. They are long-stemmed plants with unmistakable lobate leaves.

Class Coniferales

The familiar Conifers are today widely diffused throughout the world. They appeared in the Carboniferous and consolidated their position in the Permian and Triassic. The first conifers, among them the genus *Walchia* (fig. 17), were very close to present-day araucarias.

Sub-type **Angiospermae**

The angiospermae are the advanced plants, with seeds contained in a well-diversified casing and flowers, which today predominate in terrestrial plant life. Their origin is unknown, but may have occurred in the Triassic Period. Their vast diffusion began with the Cretaceous.

Class Dicotyledones

These are plants in which the seed comes with two small embryonic leaves. They appeared in the Mesozoic Era, and in the Tertiary became the dominant group. Today they make up the biggest proportion of land flora (fig. 18).

Class Monocotyledones

The most evolved plants are those in which the seed has a single embryonic small leaf. Among them is the oldest known angiosperm, the *Sanmiguelia lewisi* (fig. 19), a species found in the Triassic soils in Colorado. Monocotyledones, which include palms and Gramineae, began to develop considerably towards the end of the Mesozoic Era. The Italian Tertiary deposits have produced a number of fossil palms.

ANIMALS

Type **Protozoa**

The protozoa are animals that vary in size from one micron to several centimetres. They are mainly aquatic and unicellular. Fossilisation has preserved only those with resistant structures, a calcareous, siliceous or chitinous shell. Protozoa incorporate a vast number of species and are divided into numerous classes.

Class Sarcodina

Order Foraminifera

Foraminifera are unicellular organisms, especially marine organisms, with a calcareous or chitinous shell. Foraminifera have produced a large number of guide fossils, including those named macroforaminifera (which sometimes grew to a considerable size and had multichambered shells with a very complex structure. Among them were the *Nummulites* (fig. 20) of the Palaeocene, and the Fusulinids of the Carboniferous and the Permian. Foraminifera appeared in the Cambrian Period and are still in existence today.

Order Radiolaria

Radiolaria are unicellular marine organisms with a perforated siliceous shell which varies greatly in form and is adorned with prickles and spines (fig. 21). Radiolaria appeared in the Cambrian Period and their accumulated skeletons gave rise to solid rocky masses.

Class Ciliata

Ciliata are aquatic protozoa with a shell which can be preserved by fossilisation. The most widespread Ciliata in the fossil state are the tintinnids, which have a goblet- or tiny bell-shaped shell (fig. 22); they appeared for the first time in the Jurassic Period.

Type **Porifera**

Porifera, or sponges, are known in the fossil state from the Precambrian Period, whether in the form of complete specimens, or as siliceous or calcareous fragments, that is microscopic elements, known as spicules, which provide inner support for the body (fig. 23).

Type **Archaeocyatha**

Archaeocyathids are extinct organisms which once lived in the Cambrian seas. They were cone-shaped creatures, consisting of two concentric porous walls connected by vertical septa and horizontal tabulae (fig. 24). In the central part of the organism there was a cavity comparable to the pseudogastric cavity in sponges. Archaeocyathids lived attached to the sea bed in shallow water, near the coast-line. They were classified either as coelenterates because of their vertical radial septa, or as sponges because of their central cavity. Today they are regarded as a completely separate type. The oldest Italian fossils, found in Cambrian soils in Sardinia, belong to the Archaeocyathids.

Type **Coelenterates**

Coelenterates are aquatic animals made up basically of a central cavity with a single orifice, surrounded by a radial pattern of tentacles. They appear in two forms, one fixed or polyp, the other free or jellyfish. Polyp and jellyfish can be alternating forms in the life of a single species.
Fossil coelenterates are known from the Archaeozoic Era onwards. Impressions left by the 'umbrella' of jellyfish have been found in Archaeozoic soils. The polyp forms appeared later, in the Ordovician. From then on, coelenterates with a calcareous skeleton formed vast settlements and began to build coral reefs. Transformed and removed from geological phenomena after their formation, these today constitute certain mountains. One example is the Dolomites in Italy, which comprise remains of a coral reef built in the Triassic Period.

Class Protomedusae

These are primitive jellyfish, now extinct, whose impressions have been found in the Cambrian soils of many sites and in Precambrian rocks in North America. They are the oldest known coelenterates, similar to present-day jellyfish, but without tentacles.

Class Dipleurozoa

Dipleurozoa are jellyfish which lived during the Cambrian Period and are now non-existent. They consisted of a bell-shaped 'umbrella', grooved by a medial incision and radial grooves, and equipped with numerous filiform tentacles around the edges (fig. 25).

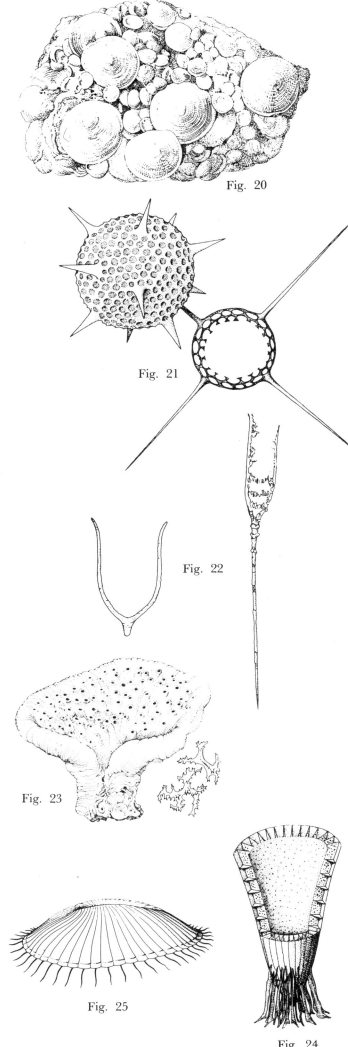

Fig. 20

Fig. 21

Fig. 22

Fig. 23

Fig. 25

Fig. 24

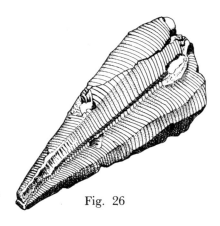

Fig. 26

Fig. 27

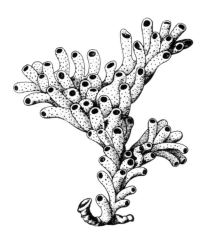

Fig. 28

Fig. 29

Class Scyphozoa

Scyphozoa are coelenterates, still living·today, which have left scanty fossil remains. They lack hard parts and are thus known chiefly from the impressions left in the sediments by the jellyfish 'umbrella'. The oldest date back to the Cambrian. A number of now extinct organisms which lived from the Cambrian to the Triassic have been attributed to this group of coelenterates. They are the Conulariida, whose 4-sided pyramid-shaped shells, between 4 and 10cms. long, acted as an external skeleton (fig. 26).

Class Hydrozoa

Hydrozoa are coelenterates which still exist today; they are found either in polyp form or as jellyfish. The polyps are in many cases equipped with a more or less calcified skeleton and thus preserve well in the fossil state. Numerous groups of encrustant Hydrozoa had in the past some importance as reef-builder organisms; among them, branched millipora that appeared in the Cretaceous, the stromatoporoids which lived from the Cambrian to the Cretaceous, and the spongiomorphida in the Triassic and the Jurassic.

Class Anthozoa

The anthozoa are a group of coelenterates which originated in the Ordovician period. Their present-day equivalents are widely dispersed in the world's seas; they comprise forms without skeletons (like sea anemones) and forms with a calcareous skeleton, and both isolated and colonial forms (fig. 27). Anthozoa with calcareous skeleton, which include red coral and builder madrepores, once constructed impressive coral reefs now transformed into rocky masses. Here it is possible to find the fossilised remains of the former reef-builders. A number of different groups have been atttributed to the Anthozoa: the alcyonarians with low-resistance skeletons (to which the red coral belongs), the zoantharians which include most of the fossil and living builder corals, and the tabulate corals, a now extinct group that lived in the seas of the Palaeozoic Era.

Type **Bryozoa**

Bryozoans are colonial animals whose external shape makes them look like coelenterates, although their anatomy is much more complex. For one thing they have a complete alimentary canal, with mouth aperture, stomach and anal aperture. The colonies of bryozoa secrete a rather thin skeleton and create branched formations which are varied and elegant in structure. Every colony contains many individuals, each of which is contained in a small cell in the skeleton (fig. 28). Bryozoa are in abundance in today's seas and were even more widespread in past geological periods. They appeared in the Ordovician and were so numerous in some seas and periods that their accumulated skeletons formed masses of bryozoan sands which, after being cemented, were transformed into solid rocks.

Type **Brachiopoda**

Brachiopods are marine animals possessing a bivalved shell and a complex anatomy, which, despite big surface differences or morphology, bring them close to the bryozoans (fig. 29); the presence of the shell means that they were easily preserved in the fossil state. Brachiopods appeared in the Cambrian Period. They were abundant in the Palaeozoic and Mesozoic, and then began to decrease in numbers in the Cenozoic Era; currently they are represented by a limited number of species. The type Brachiopoda is divided into two classes: inarticulate brachiopods, the most primitive, with chitinous or calcareous skeleton and no hinge between the two valves which are thus held together only by muscles; and articulated brachiopods with a hinged calcareous shell, formed of teeth and fossettes.

'Worms'

The many animals which are collectively termed 'worms' belong in reality to several different types. 'Worms' are soft-bodied organisms seldom found preserved in the fossil state and usually known only from the impressions and traces they have left in the deposits. From the palaeontological point of view the most interesting groups are the type Chaetognatha, the type Annelidae and the conodonts.

Type **Chaetognatha**

There is only one known fossil representative of these marine animals, the genus *Amiskwia*, discovered in the Cambrian soils of British Columbia (Canada).

Type **Annelida**

Of these worms with segmented bodies, the fossils known to us represent the class Polychaeta, a group comprising three orders.

Fig. 30

Order Vagrant

Vagrant Polychaeta are little known in the fossil state. They are soft-bodied organisms, known from the Ordovician Period principally through the traces of their toothed-jaw structures or scolecodonts.

Order Sedentary

Sedentary annelids have left numerous traces of their existence in the seas of the past in the form of living tubes, holes dug in the sea bed and calcareous living traces (fig. 30).

Order Miskoidea

Miskoidea were large-sized marine annelids, which lived during the Cambrian and became extinct at the end of that geological period. They are soft-bodied animals known from specimens preserved in a Canadian deposit.

Conodonts

Conodonts are one of the last mysteries in palaeontology. They are micro-fossils resembling small platey jaw-structures, and are very common in marine rocks formed in the period from the Ordovician to the Triassic (fig. 31). Although many scholars consider them as jaw-structures of a few types of worm, conodonts have not yet been defined with any great certainty. Some palaeontologists believe they are parts of gasteropods, cephalopods or some primitive aquatic vertebrate.

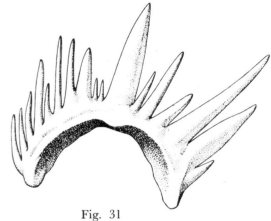

Fig. 31

Type **Arthropoda**

Arthropods are the most widely dispersed vertebrates in the natural world today and are certainly among the most evolved. Thanks to the presence of a fairly resistant chitinous external skeleton, they have lasted well in the fossil state. Arthropods are known from the Precambrian onwards.

Sub-type **Onychophora**

Also known from the Precambrian onwards, the present habitat of onycophores is completely different from the one they occupied at the start of their history (fig. 32). One of the first known onycophores, the genus *Aysheaia* from the Cambrian Period, was in fact a marine animal. Today, however, onycophores live in the humid environment of the tropical undergrowth.

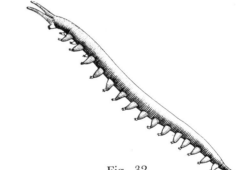

Fig. 32

Sub-type **Trilobitomorpha**

Class Trilobitoidea

Trilobitoids are primitive arthropods which lived during the Cambrian Period and possess characteristics which make them the progenitors of different groups of arthropods.

Class Trilobita

Trilobites, Palaeozoic arthropods, which appeared in the Cambrian and died out in the Permian, were marine animals distinguished by the presence of an exoskeleton divided transversely and length-wise into three parts or lobes (fig. 33). Each segment of the body had a structurally primitive pair of legs. These were all equal, except for the first pair, which were transformed into antennae. Thanks to a number of perfectly fossilised finds, the anatomy of the trilobites is known in every detail. The exceptional number of fossils has made this group extremely useful for the dating of soils of the Palaeozoic Era and has enabled the history of their evolution to be completely reconstructed.

Sub-type **Chelicerata**

Class Merostomata

These are aquatic animals now represented by the genus *Limulus*, which appeared in the Triassic Period. During the Palaeozoic Era, merostomes were very widespread in the form of the eurypterid group — giant water scorpions which sometimes grew to an enormous size (fig. 34). The genus *Pterygotus*, which lived in the Silurian and the Devonian, was about two metres long and is the largest anthropod which ever existed.

Class Arachnida

These animals are known from fossils since the Silurian, with the species *Palaeophonus nuncius*. This scorpion, from what we know of it today, was the first terrestrial animal. Of more recent origin are spiders, which appeared in the Carboniferous Period.

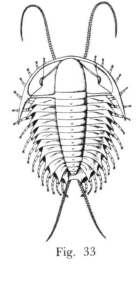

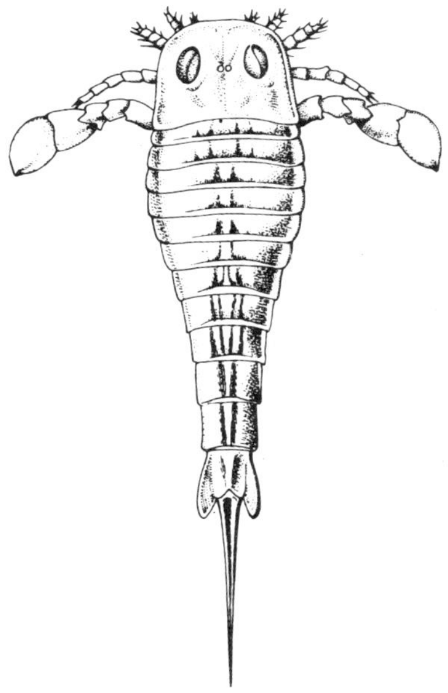

Fig. 33

Fig. 34

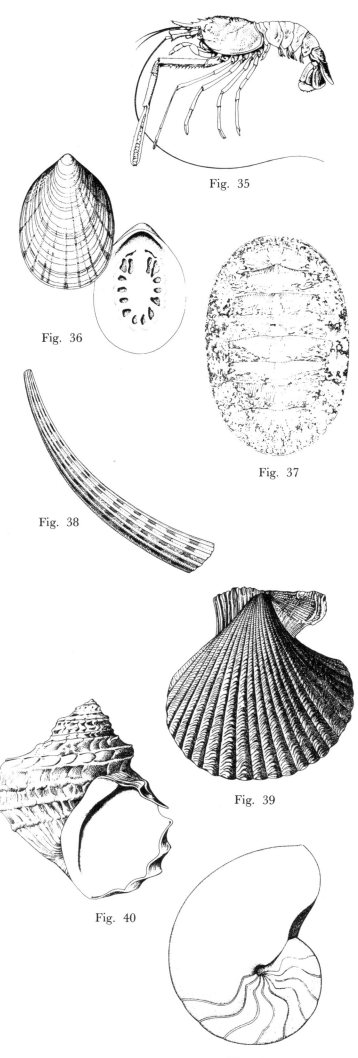

Fig. 35

Fig. 36

Fig. 37

Fig. 38

Fig. 39

Fig. 40

Fig. 41

Class Pycnogonida

These spider-like animals are very scarce as fossils; the first specimens appeared in the Devonian Period.

Sub-type **Antennates**

Class Crustacea

Crustaceans, which appeared in the Cambrian Period, are fairly common in the fossil state. The following were abundant in the seas of the past: ostracods, small crustaceans with a chitinous or calcareous shell, made of two valves, which are used as guide fossils in the relative dating of soils; cirripedes (popularly known as barnacles); aberrant crustaceans whose body is protected by a thick shell consisting of calcareous plates, which live attached to coastal rocks; and the malacostrachans, the most evolved crustaceans, to which crayfish and crabs belong. The crayfish appeared in the Triassic, and the crabs in the Jurassic (fig. 35).

Class Myriapoda

Myriapods appeared in the Devonian Period but developed only in the Carboniferous, in parallel with the development of the luxuriant forests of that time.

Class Insecta

The first insects — in wingless forms — made their appearance on the Earth during the Devonian Period. The first winged insects developed in the Carboniferous, with the group of palacoptera. The genus *Meganeura* which belongs to this group was a species of enormous dragonfly with a 70cm wing-span. Insects like arachnids and myriapods are very often found fossilised in amber, the solidified resin of ancient conifers.

Type **Mollusca**

No group of invertebrates, however broad it may be, has equalled the importance in palaeontology of the molluscs, both in their abundance and diversity, and in the value of their fossil evidence to scholars. The diffusion of molluscs in the fossil state is due to the fact that most of them have a calcareous shell which is easily preserved. They have great palaeontological interest because of the high percentage of them found in deposits, and the fact that they represent many different environments. On the one hand, therefore, having produced numerous varieties of form in the course of time, molluscs are excellent guide fossils for the relative dating of soils, while on the other, they are first-rate ecological indicators in making it possible to reconstruct the environments of the past.

Class Monoplacophora

These animals, characterised by an outer shell formed from a single hood-shaped valve, are the most primitive of all the molluscs (fig. 36). They were abundant during the Palaeozoic and were thought to be extinct until in 1952 a living monoplacophore was dredged up from the bottom of the Pacific Ocean.

Class Polyplacophora

Polyplacophores are marine molluscs with a shell made up of eight plates which articulate from one to the next (fig. 37). They are not particularly common in the fossil state. The oldest come from Cambrian soils.

Class Scaphopoda

These are molluscs with an outer calcareous shell in the form of a slightly curved tube (fig. 38). They appeared in the Ordovician Period and are today fairly plentiful in the seas.

Class Lamellibranchiata

The group of lamellibranchs (fig. 39), to which oysters belong together with mussels and many other edible molluscs, is of great value in palaeontology. One reason is the ease with which they are found in the fossil state. Another is that their presence in deposits provides very useful indications of long ago environments. Lamellibranchs appeared in the Cambrian Period and during their evolution gave rise to a large number of new groups. Some of these died out after a reasonably long period of life; others remained more or less unchanged to the present day. Among the extinct groups were the rudistans or hippurites — reef lamellibranchs with an aberrant shell that lived during the Jurassic and Cretaceous.

Class Gasteropoda

Gasteropods (fig. 40), like the lamellibranchs, are of great value in palaeontology. They developed in the Cambrian and, in the course of the Earth's history, produced a large number of different species which are used by palaeontologists as guide fossils and ecological and climatic indicators. Among the groups no longer existing are the tentaculitids, small gasteropods which lived in the Lower Palaeozoic and were distinguished by their cone-shaped shell.

Class Cephalopoda

The cephalopods, the most evolved of the molluscs, are exclusively marine animals and almost all have an inner or outer shell. They existed in great abundance during all past geological periods. Of the three sub-classes into which they are divided, only the dibranchiates are currently widespread, while the nautiloids are reduced to a few species of the genus *Nautilus* and the ammonoids disappeared at the end of the Cretaceous.

Sub-class Nautiloidea

The nautiloids (fig. 41) can still be found in the seas, but have only one representative today — the genus *Nautilus*, which has a flat spiral shell with a series of chambers inside. In the seas of the past, these animals were very widespread; during the Palaeozoic, from the Cambrian Period onwards, there were straight-shell, slightly curved shell and flat spiral shell varieties. Their decline started in the Mesozoic, when the most primitive types disappeared and the modern types of nautiloid, similar to the present *Nautilus*, came on the scene.

Sub-class Ammonoidea

The ammonoids (fig. 42), more commonly called ammonites, are a broad group of cephalopods which appeared in the Devonian Period and died out at the end of the Cretaceous. They are marine animals characterised by an outer shell which has a generally flat spiral shape, and is divided up inside into chambers by complex septa. The large number of different forms, the great rapidity of evolution and the widespread diffusion in terms of area make the ammonites excellent guide fossils for the soils of the Mesozoic Era.

Sub-class Dibranchiata

This class groups together almost all the cephalopods now living: cuttlefish, squid and octopus. Along with these must be classified the extinct group of belemnites which appeared in the Triassic Period and died out either towards the end of the Cretaceous or at the start of the Palaeogene. These were cephalopods resembling squid, with ten tentacles and a very strong inner shell, usually the only part of the animal to be preserved in the fossil state (fig. 43). As far as extant groups are concerned, the cuttlefish appeared at the end of the Mesozoic Era, the squid in the Lower Jurassic and the octopus in the Upper Cretaceous.

Type **Echinodermata**

They are complex marine animals which have well differentiated nervous, circulatory, and digestive systems. All echinoderms have a dermic skeleton which can be continuous (made up of calcareous plates), or discontinuous (consisting of separate spicules). The former is by far the more common. The continuous skeleton contains, as in a theca, all the organs, and, being very resistant, is easily preserved in the fossil state. Echinoderms appeared in the Cambrian Period and had a very complicated evolutionary life; they are divided into numerous classes, some of them totally extinct.

Class Cystoidea

These are echinoderms which lived from the Ordovician to the Devonian. They are characterised by a globular or flattened theca, formed of polygonal plates (fig. 44). The theca had a peduncle, by which the animal remained fixed to the solid substratum of the sea bed.

Class Blastoidea

The blastoids lived from the Ordovician to the Permian and were characterised by the presence of an ovoid theca, made up of thirteen main plates, but no arms or peduncle (fig. 45).

Class Edrioasteroidea

These were echinoderms with a globular or flattened body which lived fixed to the sea bed by means of the lower part of the theca, which had a number of arms, but no peduncle. The theca consisted of a large number of irregularly shaped plates and bore five sinuate ambulacral areas made up of smaller plates (fig. 46). The edrioasteroids lived from the Cambrian to the Carboniferous.

Class Crinoidea

These are the present-day sea-lilies, consisting of an ovoid theca equipped with articulated arms and a long peduncle, by which the animal attaches itself to the sea bed (fig. 47). Crinoids appeared in the Ordovician Period. They were in great abundance during the Palaeozoic Era and had a very complicated evolutionary history.

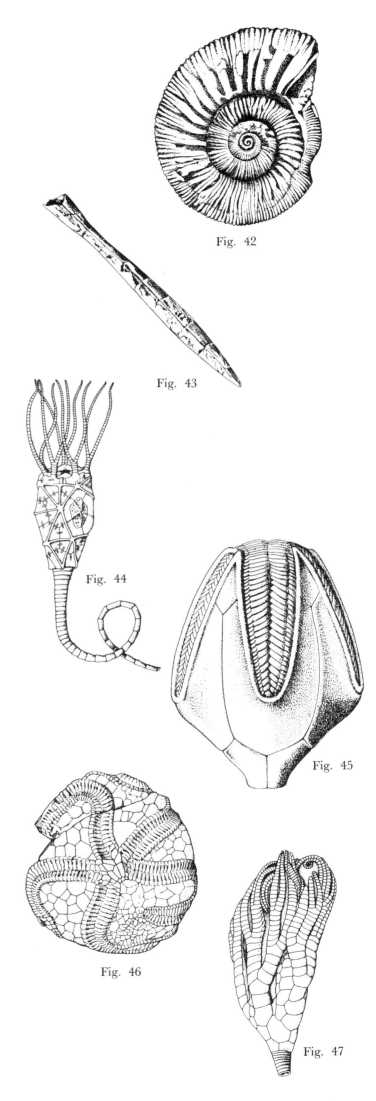

Fig. 42

Fig. 43

Fig. 44

Fig. 45

Fig. 46

Fig. 47

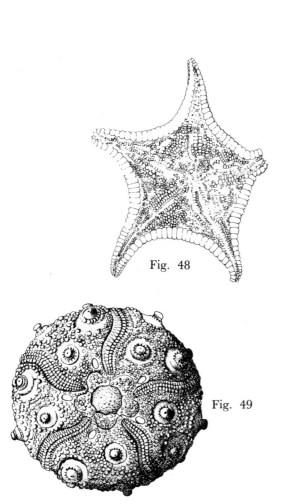

Fig. 48

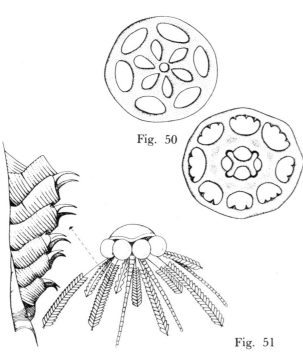

Fig. 49

Fig. 50

Fig. 51

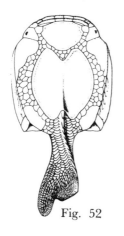

Fig. 52

Class Stelleroidea

Stelleroidea comprise the common starfish, whose evolution began in the Ordovician Period; many perfectly fossilised specimens have been discovered (fig. 48).

Class Echinoidea

Generally known as sea-urchins, Echinoidea were much more abundant in the past than they are now. The history of the echinoids began in the Ordovician Period. Two fundamentally different types of these echinoderms exist: the regular echinoids (fig. 49), or common rock sea-urchins, with a very regularly shaped theca; and irregular echinoids (fig. 30), such as sand dollars, with an irregular shaped theca and without large spicules.

Class Holothuroidea

The present-day sea-cucumbers. These echinoderms do not have a continuous outer skeleton made up of a combination of plates, but there are numerous calcareous sclerites (or limy plates) inside, with a fairly distinctive and easily recognisible form (fig. 50). In the absence of a resistant theca, the holothuroids are rarely found complete in the fossil state; isolated sclerites are, however, common in deposits. The first holothuroids appeared in the Cambrian Period.

Sub-type **Stomochordata**

Stomochordates — animals with a stomochord — are transitional between invertebrates and chordates.

Class Pterobranchiata

These are colonial organisms in which different individuals are united by a common structure, a branched chord called a stolon. Both the stolon and the various individuals in the colony are protected by a skeleton in the form of a branched tube. They are known in the fossil state from the Cretaceous Period.

Class Graptolithoidea

Graptolites, today a completely extinct group, were once widely dispersed in the seas from the Cambrian to the Lower Carboniferous. They were pelagic colonial organisms, similar to pterobranchs, and lived enclosed in a chitinous exoskeleton. The colony was made up of small superimposed annular segments and extended along a straight or curved stem that was single or branched, and bore the thecae that contained the different individual creatures (fig. 51).

Type **Chordata**

Chordates are bilaterally symmetrical animals with a very high differentiation of organs and a dorsal chord known as a notochord. They make up a group diverse both in its anatomical composition and in the general appearance of the body. Attributed to this type are animals without skeletons like the hemichordates, tunicates and cephalochordates, which are scarce in the fossil state, and animals with a bony cartilaginous internal skeleton, like the vertebrates.

Sub-type **Vertebrata**

Vertebrates are animals with a bony or cartilaginous skeleton inside the body. The skeleton consists of a stem or vertebral column comprising vertebrae — separate bony segments which protect a continuous dorsal chord. The central nervous system is situated dorsally along the chord and opens out in the front in an encephalon which is enclosed and protected in a cephalic skeleton. The principle part of the circulatory apparatus consists of a pumping organ, the heart. There are eight classes of vertebrate.

Class Agnatha

These are aquatic vertebrates, with an internal cartilaginous skeleton, but no limbs or real jawbones. These contrast with the Gnathostomata to which all the other classes of jawed vertebrates belong. To this class are attributed the most primitive and ancient vertebrates also called ostracoderms, which first appeared during the Ordovician. The class has two sub-classes.

Sub-class Cephalaspida.

Cephalaspids comprise a number of primitive agnatha which lived between the Ordovician and the Devonian. They possessed a strong outer carapace and a fairly flattened body. The modern agnatha is classed in the order of cyclostomes because of their elongated and cylindrical body, with no carapace; examples are lampreys and hagfish.

Sub-class Pteraspida

These agnatha with outer carapace lived in the seas and continental freshwater settings from the Ordovician to the Devonian (fig. 52).

Class Placodermi

Placodermi are aquatic vertebrates, now extinct, which lived during the Devonian. More evolved than the agnatha, placoderms had exterior armour-plating, movable jawbones and limbs in the form of matching front and rear fins (fig. 53). The development of movable jawbones and limbs enabled these animals to escape life on the sea-bed and become fierce and mobile predators. The most striking placoderm yet known is the genus *Dinichthys* from the Devonian Period. It had armour-plating to protect its head and front of the body, which alone could measure as much as three metres.

Class Chondrichthyans

Chondrichthyans are fish with a cartilaginous skeleton still found in abundance in modern seas as sharks, rays, mantas etc. These vertebrates, which appeared in the Devonian, comprise, in addition to the surviving groups, extinct groups such as Cladoselache and Xenacasthus (fig. 54). The modern type of selachian appeared in the Palaeozoic Era: the group Batoidei, to which rays, mantas and electric rays belong, began in the Jurassic. The group of Holocephalians, to which the present-day chimaeras belong, appeared in the Devonian.

Class Osteichthyes

Osteichthyes are fish with an ossified skeleton which now make up the major proportion of fish fauna. They are divided into the two sub-classes: Actinopterygii and Choanichthyes, both of which appeared in the Devonian Period, and whose descendants are plentiful today. Some palaeontologists place sharks in the Acanthodian group of fish, which were to some degree dispersed from the Silurian to the Permian. From the palaeontological and evolutionary points of view, the Choanichthyes have considerable importance because they are located on the evolutionary line which later led on to the terrestrial vertebrates, and so to the amphibians. The Choanichthyes comprise two groups, the Dipnoans and the Crossopterygii. The former were abundant during the Devonian, but are today restricted to a few species in the inland waters of South America, Africa and Australia. The Crossopterygii (fig. 55), direct progenitors of the amphibians, disappeared almost completely at the end of the Cretaceous; only one species survives, the *Latimeria chalumnae*, recently discovered in the waters of the Mozambique Channel.

Class Amphibia

Amphibians, derived from the Crossopterygii of the Devonian Period, were the first vertebrates to venture on to *terra firma*, but did not manage to adapt completely to the subaereal environment. Modern amphibians are very different from the Crossopterygian fish. However, there is a fossil group comprising a number of forms which possess features linking them to these Palaeozoic fish; these are the amphibian Labyrinthodonts, particularly the order *Ichthyostega*, which have the appearance of terrestrial animals with well-developed feet, but which are, in reality, intermediary between fish and amphibians.

The Labyrinthodonts (fig. 56), the primitive amphibians, and most of the Lepospondyls (another group which flourished in the Palaeozoic), disappeared between the Permian and the Triassic. The few forms which survived gave rise to modern amphibians; of these, the Anurans appeared in the Jurassic, and the Urodelans in the Cretaceous. The first reptiles originated in the Carboniferous Period from the Palaeozoic Labyrinthodonts.

Class Reptilia

Reptiles are more evolved animals than amphibians: apart from detailed anatomical features, the difference lies in the fact that reptiles relinquished the initial stage of aquatic development and formed an amniotic egg which could be laid out of the water. The reptiles appeared on the Earth in the Carboniferous Period and derive from the Embolomeres, a group of amphibian labyrinthodonts. In the Upper Palaeozoic and the Mesozoic, they evolved very rapidly and as a result came to dominate the Earth. Relatively few reptiles exist today, because of large-scale extinction that occurred at the end of the Mesozoic Era. However, fossil reptiles comprise an enormous variety of different forms, adapted to every kind of environment. During the Mesozoic Era, there were herbivorous and carnivorous reptiles, reptiles adapted to freshwater and marine life, groups adapted to the different subaereal habitats, and even flying reptiles. The class of reptilia is divided into six sub-classes on the basis of the anatomical structure of the skull and, more particularly, on the basis of the presence, absence, number and arrangement of temporal apertures. Three of these sub-classes have modern representatives still extant.

Sub-class Anapsida

Anapsids are reptiles distinguished by having a skull with no temporal apertures. They are very important in the history of vertebrate evolution because they incorporate the most primitive forms which can be considered progenitors of all fossil and living reptiles: these are the Cotylosaurs, that lived from the Carboniferous to the Triassic, some of which feature transitional anatomical characteristics between labyrinthodont and reptilian. Also attributed to the sub-class of Anapsids are chelonians, tortoises and turtles, which are therefore the most primitive reptiles surviving today. Chelonians probably developed during the Permian, and by the Triassic were already highly specialised (fig. 57).

Sub-class Lepidosauria

Lepidosauria are reptiles whose skull has two temporal apertures. They comprise the surviving groups of Squamata, or lizards and snakes, and the Rhynchocephalians, both of which appeared in the Triassic. Also included is the extinct group of Eosuchus which appeared in the Permian and died out at the end of the Cretaceous Period. During the Mesozoic, the Squamata and the Rhynchocephalians were much more abundant than

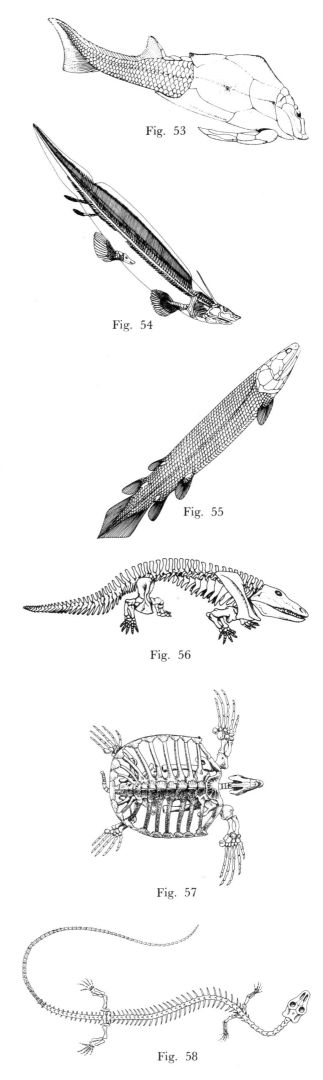

Fig. 53

Fig. 54

Fig. 55

Fig. 56

Fig. 57

Fig. 58

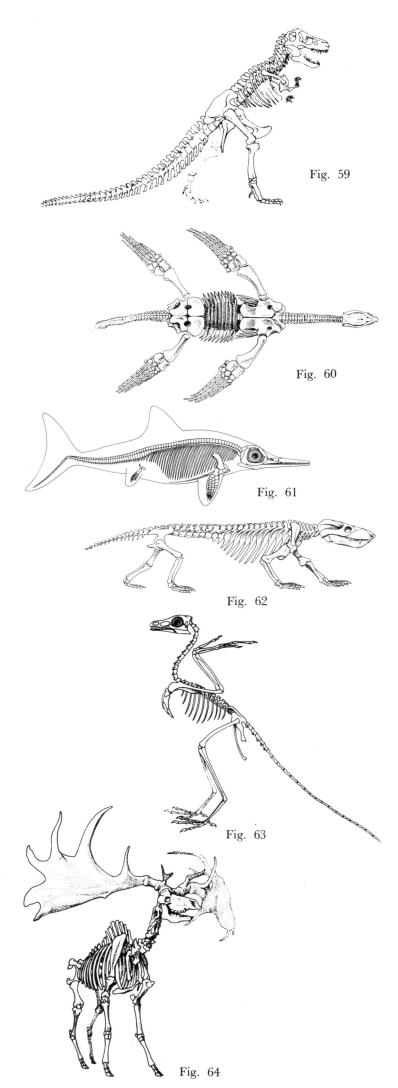

Fig. 59

Fig. 60

Fig. 61

Fig. 62

Fig. 63

Fig. 64

they are today. Among the most important are the mosasaurs. These marine Squamata, related to present-day monitor lizards, were once able to grow to 10m in length (fig. 58).

Sub-class Archosaurus

Like the Lepidosauria, archosaurs are distinguished by a skull with two temporal apertures. They are very interesting reptiles, divided into five orders, with a tendency to adopt an upright biped stance. This tendency, which led to these reptiles to use only their hindlegs for walking, naturally modified the forelegs and led to the formation of a wing structure in some groups. The flying reptiles, or pterosaurs, which lived in the Mesozoic Era, belong to the archosaur sub-class. So do the saurischian dinosaurs, the ornithischian dinosaurs which appeared in the Triassic, and the crocodiles, which also developed in the Triassic and survive to the present time (fig. 59).

Sub-class Euryapsida

These are reptiles, now extinct, distinguished by a skull with an upper temporal aperture. Euryapsids appeared in the Permian, spread widely in the Triassic, and disappeared at the end of the Cretaceous. Many reptiles who adapted to aquatic life belong to the Euryapsida, among them plesiosaurs, which lived in the Jurassic and the Cretaceous and which were able to grow longer than 10m. (fig. 60).

Sub-class Ichthyopterygia

Ichthyopterygians are reptiles perfectly adapted to aquatic life. They had a very similar body shape to modern sharks and dolphins. They appeared first in the Triassic Period, and persisted to the end of the Cretaceous, when they disappeared suddenly and totally. Unlike many other aquatic reptiles, the ichthyopterygians, or ichthyosaurs, were so well adapted to the aquatic life that they laid their eggs in the water. They were therefore ovoviviparous, a fact apparently confirmed by finds of several females which died during delivery (fig. 61).

Sub-class Synapsida

Synapsids are reptiles with a lower temporal aperture. This now extinct group lived during the Permian and Triassic Periods and were very important in the history of the evolution of vertebrates. During their history many groups of synapsids acquired some mammalian characteristics. The most evolved forms, often called reptile-mammals, represent a transitional stage between these two groups of vertebrates and gave rise to the first real mammals. The distinction between reptile and mammal, in these types of transition, is based on the position of the quadrate bone and the articular bone. In reptiles these bones are located in the skull and mandible respectively. In mammals on the other hand they have moved over to the area of the middle ear, where they have been transformed into elements used in the transmission of sound vibrations from the tympanum to the inner ear (fig. 62).

Class Birds

Birds have a very delicate skeletal structure and are rarely preserved in the fossil state. Knowledge of their evolutionary history is therefore only fragmentary. The oldest known bird is *Archaeopteryx lithographica* (fig. 63), which lived during the Upper Jurassic, a bird which had wings, but also teeth and a long tail similar to that of the reptiles. This is undoubtedly a transitional type between reptile and bird, indicating the latter's origins. More precisely, it is considered that birds derived from a group of running dinosaurs.

Birds are divided into two sub-classes: Archaeornithes which comprise only *Archaeopteryx*, and Neornithes to which all other known birds are attributed. The evolutionary explosion of birds took place at the start of the Cenozoic Era.

Class Mammalia

The mammals (fig. 64) are the most evolved vertebrates; they differ from reptiles in some important anatomical characteristics such as their warm blood and the fact that they give birth to live young. These features cannot, however, be observed from skeletal remains. The distinction between reptiles and mammals in palaeontology must therefore have an arbitrary base — on the arrangement of the quadrate bone and the articular bone, already mentioned in the case of the reptile-mammals. The oldest known fossil mammals date back to the Triassic Period: they are animals of a reduced size which belong to the group of docodonts and were not very different from some reptile-mammals. For the whole of the Triassic and the following Jurassic Periods, mammals were not especially widespread or greatly diversified. In addition to the docodonts, there were now extinct primitive groups of triconodonts, multituberculates, symmetrodonts and pantotheres. Of these, a few complete examples are known: other finds comprise only their teeth. The marsupials and the placentals originated from the pantotheres in the Cretaceous and evolved along two separate lines. Only in the Cenozoic Era did these two groups begin an evolutionary explosion connected with the disappearance of the big terrestrial reptiles. Especially in the case of the placentals, they became and remain the dominant species on Earth. Palaeontological systematics now lists 25 orders of placentals, many of which died out in the course of the Cenozoic Era. Others, however, have been preserved until the present time.

'The Classification of Fossils' from G. Pinna, *Il Grande Libro dei Fossili*, Rizzoli Editore 1976

Index

93